KU-508-932

MOTOR BOAT ENGINES

A PRACTICAL HANDBOOK
ON PETROL AND DIESEL ENGINES
AND AUXILIARY EQUIPMENT FOR
SMALL MARINE CRAFT

BY

ALAN C. WILSON

ODHAMS PRESS LIMITED
LONG ACRE, LONDON

First published 1962

© Odhams Press Ltd., 1962

T.562.N.

MADE AND PRINTED IN GREAT BRITAIN BY
ODHAMS (WATFORD) LTD., WATFORD, HERTS.

Contents

CONTENTS

Introduction

THE object of this handbook is to show the owner or operator of a modern small power craft how to obtain the best possible service from his engine and auxiliary equipment. The scope of the book covers petrol and diesel engines of both the inboard and outboard types, as used in vessels ranging from small pram dinghies up to large seagoing motor yachts and fishing craft.

In particular, the book seeks to give practical hints and advice, in the simplest possible way, to the many amateur boating enthusiasts who have come to take up cruising on lakes, rivers, canals and offshore waters in recent years. This rapidly growing army has discovered the deep satisfaction and pleasure to be had from sailing in small craft, whether as owners, hirers or club members. Many of them will already be familiar with automobile engines, but not with the special features that distinguish marine power units. The engines used in small craft are, of course, basically of the same type as those used in their millions on land, but there are important practical differences which are described in these pages.

Every aspect of the power plant is dealt with, including lubrication, cooling and exhaust arrangements, but the main emphasis is on diagnosing and curing troubles and faults of all kinds. The reader is shown how it is possible, by a logical process of deduction, to trace obscure faults with speed and certainty, even when the craft is afloat and far from any repair shop. Other chapters give advice on choosing the best type of engine for a boat, installing the power unit and drive gear, and starting and running under difficult conditions.

The book also deals fully with the ancillary equipment required in a power craft: fuel tanks and pipelines, electrical installations, reduction gear, engine controls, propellers, rudders, shafting, pumps and sanitary equipment. Finally, there are chapters on carrying out periodic inspections and overhaul and laying-up the craft; and on certain official recommendations and regulations which affect the operators of power craft.

Thus, the work covers all the mechanical gear likely to be installed

7

INTRODUCTION

in the average small craft, and it is hoped that owners will find it useful to keep a copy in a handy place on board, so that they can refer to its pages in the event of a breakdown or other trouble.

The kind co-operation of the following is acknowledged: Mr. A. W. M. Collyer, Miss P. Dawson, Mr. D. Densham, Mr. C. B. Forster, Mr. John Hall, Mr. H. B. Homer, Mr. C. N. M. Jones, Mr. R. A. Kisch, Mr. D. M. Martin, Mr. H. N. Norbury, Mr. D. Stevens, Mr. W. Temple.

Acknowledgements

The thanks of the publishers are due to the following for their kind co-operation and for permission to reproduce copyright illustrations:

Ailsa Craig Ltd.
Ajax Marine Engines Ltd.
Amal Ltd.
Automotive Products Co. Ltd.
Blake & Sons (Gosport) Ltd.
Borg & Beck Co. Ltd.
Brit Engineering Co. Ltd.
British Anzani Engineering Co. Ltd.
British Motor Corporation Ltd.
British Seagull Co. Ltd.
British Twin Disc Ltd.
Bryce Berger Ltd.
B.S.A. Ltd.
Burgess Products Co. Ltd.
C.A.V. Ltd.
Coventry-Apex Engineering Co. Ltd.
Coventry Climax Engines Ltd.
Coventry Diesel Engines Ltd.
Coventry Victor Motor Co. Ltd.
Dowty Marine Ltd.
Enfield Industrial Engines Ltd.
E.N.V. Engineering Co. Ltd.
Esso Petroleum Co. Ltd.
Ford Motor Co. Ltd.
General Motors Ltd. (AC-Delco Division)
Healey Marine Ltd.
Jabsco Pump Co. Ltd.

Leyland Motors Ltd.
Lister Blackstone Marine Ltd.
Lloyd's Register of Shipping
Lockheed Precision Products Ltd.
Joseph Lucas Ltd.
Morris Motors Ltd.
Newage (Manchester) Ltd.
Parsons Engineering Co. Ltd.
Perkins Engines Ltd.
Petters Ltd.
J. & F. Pool Ltd.
Self-Changing Gears Ltd.
Self Priming Pump Co. Ltd.
Serck Radiators Ltd.
Ship & Boat Builders' National Federation
Shorrock Superchargers Ltd.
Siba Electric Ltd.
Simmonds Aerocessories Ltd.
Simms Motor Units Ltd.
Solex Ltd.
Stuart Turner Ltd.
Teleflex Products Ltd.
John I. Thornycroft & Co. Ltd.
Trianco Ltd.
Turner Manufacturing Co. Ltd.
University Marine Ltd.
Vokes Ltd.
Watermota (1959) Ltd.
Zenith Carburettor Co. Ltd.

CHAPTER 1

Choosing a Marine Engine

IN all main respects the petrol, diesel and vaporizing oil-burning engines used in small marine craft today are identical with those installed in motor cars, motor cycles, lorries, tractors and so on. But although both types are very similar in design, the conditions under which marine engines generally operate are much more severe. The road vehicle engine seldom operates at its maximum speed; it gets frequent cooling-off periods during traffic hold-ups and when coasting downhill. Marine engines, on the other hand, run the greater part of their lives at more than 80 per cent of their maximum speed, with no traffic halts to give a respite. Furthermore, when a boat is operating in choppy waters, or even in the backwash of passing traffic, an additional strain is imposed on the engine as the craft has virtually to climb up a series of short steep hills. When the boat is sliding down the far side of a wave further strains are imposed on the engine and shafting.

Because of these exacting conditions of service, when the purchase of a marine engine is considered it is wise to choose the best unit which can be afforded. However, before buying any engine the prospective purchaser should consider what types are available and find out what can be expected from each in terms of speed and fuel cost when installed. Modern marine engines may be classified as follows: four-stroke and two-stroke petrol (or petrol-vaporizing oil) engines; four-stroke and two-stroke diesels. All these types can be further classified as being either liquid-cooled or air-cooled, and either for inboard or outboard installation.

FOUR-STROKE PETROL ENGINE

This is perhaps the most popular type of marine engine for yachts and pleasure cruisers, although the diesel is steadily gaining favour. It produces one power stroke in every four strokes of the piston, or every two crankshaft revolutions. In each cycle of operations (Fig. 1.1), the sequence of events is as follows:

1. Induction stroke. This is the first downward stroke of each cycle. It commences with the air inlet valve of the cylinder open, the piston travelling downward and sucking in through the valve a mixture of petrol vapour and

9

air from the carburettor. At the bottom of this stroke the inlet valve closes and the piston then begins to rise.

2. Compression stroke. As the piston moves upward, with inlet and exhaust valves closed, the fuel mixture is compressed until it reaches about

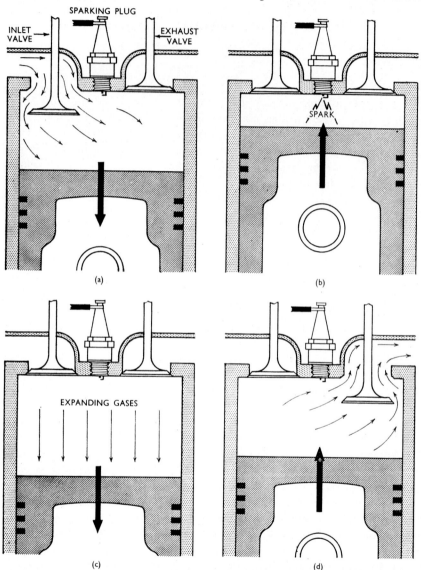

FIG. 1.1. *Four-stroke cycle, petrol engine.* (a) *Induction stroke,* (b) *ignition at end of compression stroke,* (c) *power stroke,* (d) *exhaust stroke.*

FIG. 1.2. *A small four - stroke marine petrol engine, the Coventry Victor W.N.4, with horizontally opposed twin cylinders developing 10½ b.h.p. at 1,800 r.p.m. The engine is water cooled and has magneto ignition.*

125 lb. per sq. in. (this varies slightly with different makes). Just before the piston reaches the top of its travel the compressed fuel mixture is fired or ignited by an intense electric spark which jumps across the points or gap of the spark plug. The compressed petrol-air mixture does not actually explode, but burns very rapidly. The gas thus liberated expands and forces the piston downwards on its third stroke.

3. **Power stroke.** During the greater part of this stroke both inlet and exhaust valves are closed. Just as the piston reaches the bottom of this stroke when the power of the burning gas is exhausted, the outlet or exhaust valve opens.

4. **Exhaust stroke.** As the piston rises the spent gas is forced through the open exhaust valve into the exhaust manifold, thence to the exhaust pipe to be finally discharged to the atmosphere.

A typical small four-stroke engine is shown in Fig. 1.2.

TWO-STROKE PETROL ENGINE

This type of engine gets its name from the fact that there is a power stroke to each revolution of the crankshaft. It does not have the valve mechanism of the four-stroke cycle; instead, there are openings—known as ports—in the cylinder wall, which are covered and uncovered by the piston on its up and down movement. In the usual two-stroke engine there are three such openings —the inlet, exhaust, and transfer ports. The cycle of operations—in which the crankcase plays an important part—is as follows (Fig. 1.3).

1. As the piston moves upward, it uncovers the inlet port and sucks a fresh charge of petrol/air mixture into the crankcase, at the same time compressing the fuel charge left in the cylinder by the previous cycle.

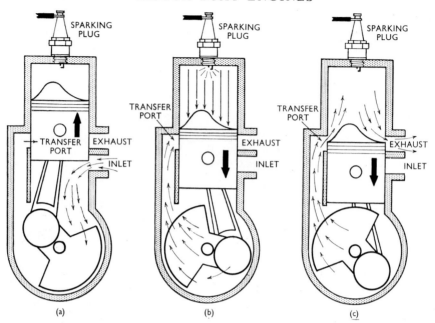

FIG. 1.3. *Two-stroke cycle, petrol engine.* (a) *Induction and compression stroke,* (b) *power stroke after ignition,* (c) *exhaust and transfer ports uncovered.*

FIG. 1.4. *A two-stroke marine petrol engine, the Stuart P55ME, with vertical twin cylinders developing 8 b.h.p. at 1,500 r.p.m. The engine is water cooled and has magneto ignition.*

12

2. At the top of the stroke, ignition takes place as in the four-stroke cycle, and the piston is forced downward on its power stroke. This action also lightly compresses the charge of mixture waiting in the crankcase, the inlet port now being covered. As the piston continues its downward movement, it uncovers the exhaust port to allow the burnt gas to escape, and almost at the same moment uncovers the transfer port to pump the fresh charge from the crankcase into the cylinder.

3. Upward movement of the piston closes the exhaust and transfer ports again, opens the inlet port, and repeats the cycle.

A two-stroke engine is shown in Fig. 1.4.

DIESEL ENGINES

A diesel engine, of course, uses heavy oil as the fuel instead of petrol. It has no electrical ignition system, the principle being that air is heavily compressed by the piston and its temperature rises in consequence; the heat is then sufficient to ignite the oil which is sprayed into the cylinder. Gases are thus liberated which expand and drive the piston downwards as in a petrol engine. The complete cycle of operations of the four-stroke diesel (Fig. 1.5) is as follows:

1. Induction stroke. On the first stroke the inlet valve is open and clean air only is drawn into the cylinder by the descending piston.

2. Compression stroke. With both the inlet and exhaust valves closed, the piston rises and the charge of air is compressed until it occupies only about one-fifteenth of the total volume of the cylinder. This 1-to-15 compression ratio, as it is called, is higher in some engines and lower in a few others. The air is compressed at this point to about 500 lb. per sq. in. compared with the 125 lb. per sq. in. of the petrol engine, and its temperature in the cylinders consequently rises to as much as 1,000 deg. F. In fact, it is "red hot." With this hot air trapped between the piston and the underside of the cylinder head, a charge of diesel fuel oil is injected under pressure into the cylinder by means of a special injection pump. The fuel oil, ignited by the hot air, at once begins to burn and the expanding gases force the piston downwards.

3. Power stroke. During the greater part of this stroke the fuel oil burns steadily and not suddenly as in the petrol engine where the vapour is ignited by a spark. At the bottom of this stroke the exhaust valve opens.

4. Exhaust stroke. The spent gas is exhausted through the open valve and exhaust system as the piston moves upward.

The two-stroke diesel engine works on very similar principles to the two-stroke petrol engine. However, air is not always sucked into the crankcase to be forced into the cylinders through transfer passages, being more frequently sucked or forced by blowers directly into the cylinder. The cycle is illustrated in Fig. 1.6, and is as follows:

The piston travelling upward compresses the air and fuel is pumped into the cylinder near the top of this stroke. As the fuel burns and forces the piston downwards, exhaust ports are uncovered about halfway down the cylinder

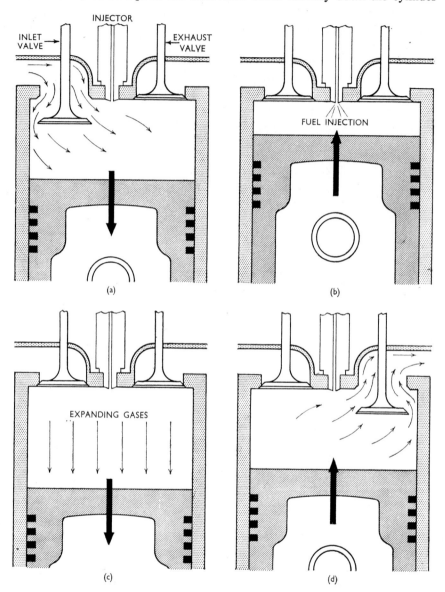

FIG. 1.5. *Four-stroke cycle, diesel engine.* (a) *Air induction stroke,* (b) *injection at end of compression stroke,* (c) *power stroke,* (d) *exhaust stroke.*

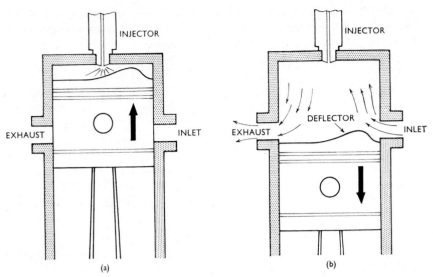

FIG. 1.6. *Two-stroke cycle, diesel engine.* (a) *Fuel injection at end of compression stroke,* (b) *exhaust and inlet ports uncovered at end of power stroke.*

and the exhaust gases escape into the exhaust pipe. At the same moment, the air inlet port is uncovered and fresh air enters the cylinder. This incoming air helps to sweep out, or scavenge, the spent gases, before both inlet and exhaust ports are again covered by the piston and another compression stroke is started. A four-stroke diesel is illustrated in Fig. 1.7, and two-stroke diesels in Figs. 1.8 and 1.11. Some two-stroke diesels have exhaust valves in the cylinder head, and are known as uniflow engines. Their principle is illustrated in Fig. 1.9.

Diesel engines further fall into two main types: "direct-injection" and "indirect-injection." Direct-injection engines have the fuel sprayed directly into the upper part, or combustion chamber as it is called, of the cylinder; whereas the combustion chamber of indirect-injection engines takes the form of an antechamber, as shown in Fig. 1.10.

VAPORIZING-OIL ENGINES

These engines work on the same principle as the petrol engine, the only difference being in the construction of the carburettor which is designed to operate on both petrol and vaporizing oil (kerosine or paraffin oil). Petrol is used to start the engine and run it until warm. Then the supply is cut off by pulling a control and vaporizing oil instead enters the carburettor where it is vaporized and passed to the engine intake manifold. The carburettors and manifolds on these engines are designed with special "hot spots" to help in the vaporization of the less volatile fuel oil. A full description of a typical V.O.-petrol carburettor is given on page 93. Fig. 1.12 is an example of an engine which can run on petrol or vaporizing oil.

OUTBOARD ENGINES

Outboard engines are being increasingly used to power a large variety of craft, from the smallest dinghies to speedboats, racing craft and quite large cabin cruisers. These units have a power head, a drive shaft extending downward, and a propeller. Both petrol and diesel types are manufactured.

The power head includes the cylinders, crankcase, crankshaft, pistons, connecting-rod assemblies, magneto system, carburettor and fuel tank. Some types are fitted with separate fuel tanks carried within the hull, however. The lower unit transmits the engine power to the propeller and includes the transmission gears, drive and propeller shafts, water pump, exhaust outlet, propeller and bracket.

Outboard engines are portable and can be fixed to the transoms of most small boats without trouble. With some hull types a special attachment may have to be used to give the necessary support. Outboard engines are dealt with in more detail in Chapter 10.

FIG. 1.7. *Representative of the many four-stroke marine diesel engines available, the Lister FR40 is a four-cylinder unit developing 40 b.h.p. at 2,000 r.p.m., with indirect fuel injection and closed-circuit water cooling.*

Fɪɢ. 1.8. *A large two-stroke diesel, the Rootes Lister TS3 has three horizontal parallel cylinders with two opposed pistons per cylinder. The engine has direct fuel injection, closed-circuit cooling, and, supercharged by blower, develops 110 b.h.p. at 2,000 r.p.m.*

LIQUID AND AIR COOLING

Small marine engines, both petrol and diesel, are available with either liquid cooling or air cooling. With the liquid-cooled type, water is sucked into the system from outside the hull by means of a small engine-driven pump. It passes through the engine's cooling jackets and is finally discharged either through the exhaust pipe, after it has cooled the exhaust manifold, or directly overboard. A refinement is to use fresh water to cool the cylinder block, cylinder head, etc. In this system, which is by far the better for a craft which will operate continually in salt water, the fresh water in the closed circuit is used over and over again. It is cooled by "raw" water which is drawn in from outside the hull and discharged over the side. Both methods are described in Chapter 11.

Air-cooled engines are gaining an increasingly large share of the marine market. Their advantages are that the engine unit is often complete in itself, it has fewer parts to require attention, and no cooling water circuit is needed. The air-cooled unit may be a little noisier in operation but this can be offset by using sound-deadening materials in the engine compartment. These engines are now available in many sizes for powering a wide range of craft.

17

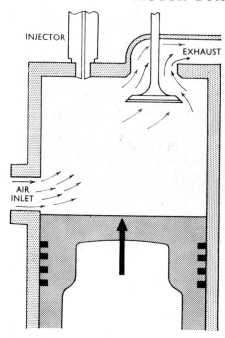

INJECTOR

EXHAUST

AIR
INLET

FIG. 1.9. *The "uniflow" two-stroke diesel system employs a valve-operated exhaust, and scavenging is assisted by the fresh charge of air admitted under pressure.*

Examples of water-cooled and air-cooled engines of similar power are shown in Fig. 1.13 and Fig. 1.14, and a smaller air-cooled diesel in Fig. 1.15.

CHOICE OF HORSE-POWER

Having decided on the type of engine to be used, the important question of horse-power must next be considered. It would obviously be just as unsatisfactory to buy a large engine for a small boat as to place a very small engine in a large craft. The owner must, therefore, arrange to install an engine which is suitable for the length, breadth, hull shape, and speed required. These are extremely important factors. For instance, a narrow 30 ft. shallow-draught launch might easily achieve a speed of 15 knots with an engine rated 30 h.p. But if the same engine were installed in a broad-beam, deeper-draught, cruising craft, a speed of 15 knots would never be attained—it would more likely be around 8 knots.*

Hull shape and design must thus enter prominently into all power calculations. The shape of the hull is very important. Power-boat shapes normally met with are: (1) the round bottom in which there is a curve almost from the deck edge to the keel; (2) the flat bottom which has a sharp curve or turn at each side; and (3) the V-bottom which rises at an angle from each side of the keel. There are many other hull forms, particularly in the case of auxiliary sailing vessels. Whenever possible the boat designer's advice on suitable engine horse-power and propeller speed should be obtained.

The smallest craft, from 6 ft. to 12 ft., include prams, dinghies, row boats, small day cruisers and auxiliary sailing vessels. Most of this class can be engined with a small outboard motor or directly driven by an inboard diesel

---

* A knot is a speed of one nautical mile (6,080 ft.) per hour. This is approximately 1$\frac{1}{16}$ land or statute miles per hour.

or petrol engine rated between 1¼ and 8 h.p. Air-cooled engines such as that shown in Fig. 1.2 are ideally suited for this class.

Extremely economical small petrol engines complete with reverse gears are also on the market. A typical 1½ b.h.p. model made by one company and weighing just 120 lb. is capable of pushing along a fair-sized dinghy or small sailing craft with a fuel consumption of less than two pints per hour. A larger diesel engine rated 4 b.h.p. and suitable for launches, day cruisers and sailing craft burns about 1½ pints of diesel fuel per hour. An 8 b.h.p. engine also in this class uses approximately one-third of a gallon every hour. A 7 h.p. air-cooled engine used in tests on the Thames was found to average 20 land miles per gallon. However, the speed and fuel economy that will be obtained in individual cases depends very much on the weight to be moved along and the hull shape.

For small craft used as tenders the larger two- and four-cylinder outboards are most suitable as they allow the maximum amount of space for

FIG. 1.10. *Cylinder head of the Perkins Four/99 diesel engine sectioned to show the position of the indirect-injection combustion chamber.*

passenger use. Again, craft to be carried on car tops cannot normally be fitted with an inboard engine but an outboard can easily be carried in the boot.

Next in size come the large row boats, some converted lifeboats, general harbour craft, big tenders, launches, and cruisers between 12 ft. and 20 ft.

FIGS. 1.11 and 1.12. *Two popular marine engines of similar power. The Stuart H2M* (left) *is a twin-cylinder two-stroke diesel developing 9 b.h.p. at 1,500 r.p.m. The Brit E10* (right), *also a twin, can operate on petrol or vaporizing oil, developing 10 b.h.p. and 8 b.h.p. with the respective fuels at 1,000 r.p.m.*

on the waterline. For these, the larger air-cooled and smaller water-cooled petrol and diesel engines are ideal. There is a very wide selection of such units available.

Air-cooled inboard engines might well have a slight advantage if the speed range is to be within the 6—8 m.p.h. limit, their installation being simple. Where higher speed is required and a great deal of weight has to be pushed along, as in the case of many day cruisers, the two-cylinder petrol and diesel water-cooled engines should be considered. If an inboard engine is used it should be fitted with reverse and reduction gears.

Above the 20 ft. waterline length the inboard water-cooled engine comes into its own. Fitted with stout covers, they are much quieter in operation than the large outboard units, and produce little heat. Their cost of installation is, however, higher, as fuel tanks, exhaust lines, cooling system hook-ups, and starting battery are needed. Above a waterline length of about 30 ft. the twin-screw installation may have to be considered.

A few further hints may be of assistance to the owner who is in doubt about choosing the best type of engine. If the boat is to spend its time cruising at easy speeds from one place to another or exploring little-known reaches and rivers, a speed of 8 to 10 knots should be ample. Larger engines to give greater speed can be fitted, but it is not good policy to install a high-power engine which will rarely be called upon to run full out. It will take up much more space and its fuel and maintenance bills will be proportionately higher.

CHOOSING A MARINE ENGINE

Most people realise that the cost of petrol or diesel oil consumed rises as the speed increases but few realise how steeply the fuel costs can climb. A rule-of-thumb for estimating fuel consumption is that it is in the direct proportion to the speed of the boat raised to the third power. In simple language this means that if a boat uses two gallons per hour at a speed of 10 knots, then to make 20 knots or twice the speed it will use 16 gallons (assuming that the hull is designed to attain such a speed).

A cruising speed of 8 to 10 knots should be enough for the average small boat operator, with a reserve of 2 knots. Twelve knots is a pretty good speed and as fast as anyone will care to travel when the water is not smooth. At 15 knots any craft will start to "bump" if the water is even slightly choppy.

Whether the hull is to be powered by a diesel or a petrol engine is another matter the boat owner must decide. The diesel is more efficient than the petrol engine, in the mechanical sense. In most petrol engines only about 18 to 20 per cent of the energy present in the fuel is converted into propeller-turning power. Something like 80 per cent is lost through friction between moving parts, through heat losses to the cooling water or cooling air, and in the exhaust gases. A diesel, however, makes available about 34 to 35 per cent of the power contained in a similar amount of fuel. So, on one gallon of fuel a diesel engine should be able to push a craft twice as far as a petrol engine of the same horse-power.

These facts may suggest to the reader that all boats should be fitted with diesels. It must be remembered, however, that the diesel is more expensive to manufacture than its petrol counterpart. The following are pointers to deciding whether a diesel should be used in a boat:

1. If cost has not to be considered a diesel should be installed for preference.

2. If the craft is to be used only for summer weekends, holiday cruises, etc., a petrol engine may well be cheaper to run.

3. If the boat is to be used extensively a diesel will be more economical.

It will be seen that whether a diesel or a petrol engine should be installed depends on the amount of work or use it will have, particularly if the hull is a big one. Where a great deal of work is expected it is more economical to purchase a diesel as the saving in fuel bills over an extended period will offset the higher initial cost. There is also the important point that diesel fuel does not present the same fire hazard as petrol.

BUYING SECONDHAND

The purchase of a secondhand engine for any craft is something that should be approached with caution. It must be remembered that an engine which looks spick and span with shining brass and copper pipe-work may be fit only for the scrap heap, whereas an engine that is dirty and apparently

FIGS. 1.13 and 1.14. *Water cooling in a closed circuit system is featured by the Parsons Marlin* (above), *a version of the Ford 6D six-cylinder diesel giving 65 b.h.p. at 1,600 r.p.m. Air cooling by belt-driven fan is used on the four-cylinder Petter PD4RMR diesel* (below) *which gives 52 b.h.p. at 1,800 r.p.m.*

neglected may well be in excellent running order. It is as well to remember that a pot of paint costs little but a new set of bearings will cost a great deal. The moral is, therefore, do not buy an engine on appearance alone.

A well-made marine engine, even if it receives the minimum amount of attention, will last very many years. It will outlive comparable motor-car engines by generations. Usually it is used only during the mid-six months of the year and then, in the case of most pleasure craft, for week-ends only. However, it is no use buying an engine if it has been mishandled or not correctly maintained, and the intending purchaser of an engine should watch for signs of maltreatment.

When looking at a secondhand unit, first make a careful examination of the exterior of the cylinder block for any indication of repairs to the outside metal walls or the water jackets. Fractures that have been repaired are usually caused by insufficient cooling or by freezing of the water inside the jackets.

Welded repairs to water jackets can be effectively carried out by specialists in this kind of work. A cylinder block which has been thus repaired by welding should not be condemned out of hand, but such a repair should reduce the purchase price to at least 20 per cent below that of a similar engine which has not been subject to such damage.

If the repair looks good the prospective purchaser should ask when it was made. If it was made some time previously and the boat has since been operated without trouble then the engine can be considered to be in good condition as far as the repair is concerned. If it is a new repair, however, and the boat has not since been used, then a certain amount of doubt must be entertained as to its trustworthiness.

For one thing, any tradesman-welder or good amateur engineer might be able to make a very presentable-looking weld to a cracked water jacket—until the engine is placed in operation and the cylinder block warms up. Then it can easily happen that the metal adjoining the welded area fractures and the entire job has to be repeated—that is, if the block is not beyond further repair. To make a good weld it is often necessary to heat the entire cylinder block before the actual welding of the fracture is attempted. This pre-heating reduces the possibility of the block warping or buckling either when the weld is made or when the entire block is cooling off after the job has been completed. In practice it reduces the possibility of stresses and strains, which can lead to further fractures being set up.

Should an exterior fracture develop in the walls of a water jacket, it may be possible to bolt or screw a patch over the damaged area. Such repairs are sometimes quite effective but must always be regarded as a temporary measure only.

Where possible the advice of the engine manufacturer or a competent welding specialist should be obtained regarding cylinder block fractures. Often the manufacturer's representative is able to supply a new block at a very reasonable price, or else a good waterside mechanic can suggest a machine shop where a secondhand replacement block might be obtained.

It is always useful to know the age of an engine. Engines do not have birth certificates, but the number of years which have elapsed since the unit left the factory can always be ascertained by writing to the maker and quoting the serial number, which is usually cast into the metal of the cylinder block or crankcase.

Even knowing the age of an engine does not tell whether it has been little or much used, so it is essential to check the general condition by carrying out one or two practical tests.

The simplest is to check the compression of each of the cylinders by hand-cranking the engine and, with the spark plug or fuel injector removed, placing the heel of the palm of the hand over each cylinder opening in turn as the piston is rising on the compression stroke (both valves closed). The compression of the air caused by the rising piston can then be felt distinctly. If there is a marked difference between the amount of compression in one cylinder and the others, the piston rings in the low-compression cylinder are badly worn.

To check further, turn over the engine until the piston of that particular cylinder is at the bottom of its compression stroke, replace the spark plug or fuel injector, then remove the oil filler cap. Holding an ear close to the filler opening, get someone to turn the engine slowly in its direction of rotation so that the piston in the cylinder under test is rising. If a distinct hissing sound is heard then the piston rings or cylinder or both are worn. If there is a heavy gust of compressed air it is quite possible that they are badly worn.

If such conditions exist in more than one cylinder the cylinder head should be lifted and the cylinder bores accurately measured for out-of-roundness. If this is excessive the engine will have had a great deal of use and probably needs a general overhaul before it can again be put into service. If there is no hissing sound but the engine can be turned over fairly easily by hand, the valves may be leaking and need to be renewed, refaced, or merely ground-in by hand to their seatings.

A further test for ring tightness can be made by removing the spark plugs or injectors, then pouring a quantity of paraffin or engine oil into each cylinder. If the oil soon drips away into the crankcase the rings or cylinder walls must be worn. If the vendor says that they "will take up when the engine is running," don't believe him. Alternatively, a heavy lubricating oil can be squirted into cylinders under test, and the engine turned by hand. If this requires greater effort than before the oil was poured in, it is a certain indication of ring or cylinder wear.

FIG. 1.15. *Cooling air in the single - cylinder Enfield 100 diesel is drawn into the cowling by fan integral with the flywheel. Developing 7 s.h.p. at 1,800 r.p.m., this compact engine is suitable for working a small day cruiser or an auxiliary sailer.*

If the cylinder head is removed, a simple test can be made to check the general condition of the crankshaft and bottom end bearings. Press down on the piston top while a second person gently and slowly hand-cranks the engine. If the crankshaft moves without corresponding movement of the piston there must be considerable play in either the connecting rod (bottom end) bearings or the gudgeon pin. It is more likely to be in the connecting rod bearings.

Play in the crankshaft thrust bearings can also be checked by taking hold of the flywheel and vigorously pulling and pushing it in line with the crankshaft. On a typical four-cylinder engine the maximum clearance allowed by the manufacturers is only 0·012 in. If play is excessive, indicated by a slight but definite thud when the shaft is pushed or pulled against the crank cheek and the thrust washer, it is quite possible that all the main bearings are worn and need adjusting or replacing. This can be quite an expensive job.

If the craft is afloat a trial run should be made. Apart from observing the running of the engine, check all petrol and oil piping for leaks and ensure that the exhaust water-cooling system (where fitted) is working efficiently. This is shown by water "burping" from the tail pipe of the exhaust when the engine is running dead slow.

When the engine is running and has reached normal operating temperature it should be quickly accelerated and then just as quickly the speed should be reduced to idling. Worn bearings may then be indicated by particular noises in the engine. Sharp knocks will be heard if there is wear in the connecting-rod assemblies. To test further cut out each cylinder in turn. With a petrol engine this can be done by shorting out each plug; and with a diesel by disconnecting the fuel line to the injector of the cylinder under test. The rapid-acceleration test should then be repeated for each cut-out cylinder. If a distinct slapping sound develops, either the connecting rod bottom end ("big end") or the gudgeon pin in that particular cylinder needs attention.

If there is a low dull thud when speed is reduced this can be an indication of worn crankshaft bearings. Piston slap, indicated by a distinct slapping sound when the engine is running at low speed with full load, means that there is looseness in the pistons due to worn rings or cylinders. It may not be apparent when the engine is running full out or is idling. Piston slap is often present when an engine is cold but soon disappears when working temperatures are developed. Under these circumstances it can be ignored.

A light thud which seems to come and go may be due to a worn gudgeon pin or gudgeon-pin bearings, although this is not always so. The noise comes and goes as the gudgeon pin moves in its bearings.

FIG. 1.16. *Ford automobile and industrial petrol and diesel engines are the basis of several well-known marinized conversions. For example, the 59OE six-cylinder diesel, shown in section, is used for the Thornycroft engine shown in Fig. 1.17.*

FIG. 1.17. *Thornycroft RF6/D diesel engine, developing 78 b.h.p. at 2,000 r.p.m.*

FIG. 1.18. *A smaller example from the Thornycroft range of marine diesels, the RJD2 twin-cylinder develops 16 b.h.p. at 1,800 r.p.m. Easy hand starting is provided by a decompressor which automatically returns to full compression.*

MOTOR BOAT ENGINES

POWERING CONVERTED HULLS

When a craft without an engine is being acquired, and it is intended to fit an engine, the purchaser should remember that because of the build of the boat it may not be possible to locate the propeller shaft in the usual position over the hull centre line. With a ship's lifeboat, for example, the shaft may have to be mounted at an angle to the centre line. This can make the control of the craft more difficult at low speed, while there will be a tendency for the propeller to throw the boat off course unless enough starboard or port helm is carried to offset it.

Another disadvantage with many converted hulls is that the engine's fuel consumption proves to be much greater than that of a craft designed as a power boat. It must also be remembered that conversions, especially second-hand ones, are not easy to sell.

Craft that have been designed purely for sailing are sometimes converted for use as motor boats, and a further warning must be given concerning these. Although excellent craft under sail, they may not be quite as successful as power boats because not all hull forms are suitable for powering to give rated speeds. A 20 h.p. engine in a motor boat might give a speed of 15 knots, but fitted in a sailing craft it may give no more than 7 knots. Too much should not be expected in the way of performance from such conversions.

MARINIZED AUTOMOBILE ENGINES

The term "conversion" is often applied not only to converted hulls but also to describe certain types of engines. These are marinized versions of well-known automobile engines made by road vehicle manufacturers, more and more of which are being used to power marine craft. It should at once be emphasised that this does not mean that the would-be motor-boat owner can just walk into a scrap yard and buy any discarded car engine for his craft which can be "converted" by merely adding a suitable engine base. These conversions are, in fact, engineered to produce a propulsion unit comparable to any engine especially designed for marine work.

People who think that any engine can be used in a motor boat can let themselves in for many expensive shocks. As explained earlier, marine engines as used in most modern small craft are cooled by either "raw" or fresh water circulating through the engine jackets and other cooling spaces (especially around the exhaust manifold), or by air carefully ducted to hit the hot fins cast into the cylinder surfaces in the case of air-cooled engines. The motor car engine, however, is kept at running temperature by water circulating through a fan-cooled radiator system, and by the circulation of cool air around the engine as the vehicle passes over the road. The cool air also passes over the underside of the engine.

Installing a car engine in the engine compartment of a boat would rob it

FIG. 1.19. *An example of the modern marinized automobile engine, the high-speed Austin-Healey 75 develops 75 b.h.p. at 4,500 r.p.m. and is equipped with twin S.U. carburettors, direct sea-water cooling and hydraulic reverse gear mechanism.*

of the necessary supply of cooling air on all exterior surfaces, with the result that overheating would soon develop. Even if fitted with some form of radiator to supply cool air and water to the jackets, the problem of removing surplus heat from the exhaust manifold would remain. Manufacturers of marine conversions overcome these difficulties by making special manifolds to fit the engines, and also supply suitable water pumps to circulate the coolant through the system.

Several firms produce marinized versions of engines fitted to mass-produced cars and commercial vehicles, and also industrial engines, for petrol, diesel and vaporising oil. One important advantage of using such an engine is that with the modern motor manufacturer's national and international after-sales service, spare parts are easily obtainable, being often held even by small garages in out-of-the-way ports.

Typical of this class of power unit are the Thornycroft engine shown in Fig. 1.17, and the Austin-Healey 75 marine unit shown in Fig. 1.19. Others are the Parsons Marlin (Fig. 1.13) and the Ford Consul (Fig. 6.1).

CHAPTER 2

Engine Installation

AN engine should not be placed in just any position in the hull of a pleasure craft. It must be installed where its weight does not affect the boat's trim to such an extent that when under way the vessel gives the appearance of either perpetually climbing a steep hill or else sinking bow first.

Exceptions are fast runabouts and racing craft using specially designed hulls in which the bow "planes" or lifts out of the water to give the desired speed. The position the power unit is to occupy should be clearly marked by the designer on the hull construction drawings. If not, the advice of a boat builder or a naval architect should be obtained. Failing this, the hull can be compared with a similar one in which the engine installation has proved satisfactory. From such a comparison the position of the engine can easily be decided.

An old rule-of-thumb still practised is to locate the engine at the widest point of the hull, usually amidships, or one frame behind the amidship mark.

It is far better, however, to install the engine over the centre of gravity of the hull. This is a position which the designer arrives at after a series of complicated mathematical calculations taking into consideration the hull shape, weight (displacement), draught, length, beam, freeboard, and the space available for accommodation. Such calculations are beyond the ability of most amateurs, but it is possible to obtain a reasonably accurate position by simple trial-and-error methods.

To do this the engine bed is first constructed and fitted inside the hull. It should consist of two longitudinal bearers which are bolted or screwed to the bottom of the boat, that is, through the planking and some of the frames. The bearers should be at least twice as long as the engine, allowing sufficient margin to fit the engine in several temporary positions until the correct one is found.

FITTING ENGINE BEARERS

Bearers are placed accurately each side of the hull centre line in a single-screw craft and should be of hardwood. The best timber is seasoned oak, although this is sometimes difficult to work. However, it will stand the pull of the screws and bolts without splitting or bending and is highly resistant to rot caused by fresh or salt water, including bilge water which is often contaminated with grease and oil. Softwood is not generally suitable though the better quality is sometimes used. Green timber (timber that has not been seasoned) or timber that has a natural "twist" should be avoided.

The bearers must be sufficiently wide to accommodate the engine feet easily. A width of 2 in. is about the minimum, increasing to 3 in. in craft up to 30 ft. with engines not exceeding 40 h.p., and up to $4\frac{1}{2}$ in. for engines rated up to 125 h.p. As stated, the length should be more than twice that of the engine where possible, an additional advantage of long bearers being that the weight of the engine and the thrust of the propeller are distributed more evenly throughout the hull and there is no excessive strain on any particular hull area. Furthermore, if there is vibration, which can arise in the best-planned installations because of characteristics of some types of engines at certain speeds, it will be more effectively deadened if spread over a larger surface.

When the length of the engine bearers has been determined, the lower part of the bearer timber should be planed to fit the contours of the hull bottom and notched to fit over the hull frames. Marking of the lower surface

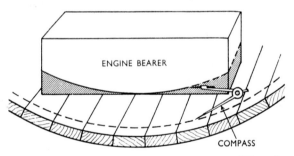

FIG. 2.1. *Marking off, or "spiling", an athwartship bearer to fit the hull. The shaded portion of the bearer will be removed.*

is best done by placing each bearer upright on the frames and pencilling the position of the frames and the slope of the hull with a compass. Professional boat builders call this "spiling", and the principle, as applied to an athwartship bearer, is shown in Fig. 2.1. Some engine erectors use cardboard templates and transfer the marks to the timber on the workbench.

When marked, the bearer notches which fit over the frames are cut and the base planed to fit the slope, if any, of the hull bottom. The amount of planing required depends on where the engine is to be placed. If it is a small auxiliary which will be located in the stern of a sailing vessel, the rise of the timbers towards the stern post may be very sharp and entail considerable plane work.

Next, the engine bearers may have to be planed to give them the correct rake (Fig. 2.2). Marine engines do not operate on a level plane, but (with

(Right) Fig. 2.2.
*Engine bearer
planed, notched and
drilled, ready to fit.*

BOLT HOLE
NOTCH
SLOPING BEARER SURFACE
SLOT FOR
NUT PLATE

(Left) Fig. 2.3.
*Marine engines are
normally mounted
sloping towards the
stern, to give the
propeller clearance.*

ENGINE
BEARER

certain exceptions) slope towards the stern. If this were not done difficult hull problems would have to be surmounted as the propeller shaft would pass through the craft's stern timbers or planking near a point where the rudder is mounted. The free flow of water to the propeller, which is essential for efficient propulsion, would then be impeded and the engine's effective pushing power greatly reduced. The mounting of the rudder would also be troublesome under such conditions. By inclining the angle of the engine and shaft the propeller is able to turn in a stream of water which is not excessively impeded by the hull structure (Fig. 2.3).

Engine makers recommend the correct angle at which their units should be installed. In general it does not exceed 15 deg. If the angle is too steep the engine can sustain damage through oil failing to reach all the moving parts. Some manufacturers insist that this aft raking angle, as it is sometimes termed, must be less than 5 deg. Others include the bow lift of the craft when travelling at full speed in the maximum figure, and it must be taken into consideration when cutting the top bearer surface. Sometimes further cutting is necessary to accommodate flywheel housings, gearbox casings, etc.

When completed, the bearers can be joggled over the frames and lightly attached to the hull with screws. Bearers must be equidistant from the centre-line; this can be measured from the keel. Transverse supports can be placed between the bearers to obtain greater rigidity if they are fairly high—and it should be remembered that due allowance must be made for those portions of the engine projecting below the level of the bearers (Fig. 2.4), with clearance for ventilation, lifting tackle, and so. The stretchers, as these supports are called, must be placed so that air can pass freely beneath them. This helps to cool the hot oil in the sump and oil pan. Two stretchers should be sufficient. All screws, bolts and studs used should be galvanised or of rust-resistant materials to withstand corrosion.

Spotting the holes through which the bearer-to-hull bolts pass demands great accuracy in marking out. Then pilot holes of a suitable size should be drilled and afterwards enlarged to bolt diameter. This will avoid the chance of mistakes. The screws or bolts must pass through the bottom of the boat (the skin), through each of the frames which are to support the bearer, and into the bearer timber. Screws should enter the wood for at least two-thirds of the bearer depth. Bolts must pass through completely and the nuts tightened on to large washers. Where a nut interferes with the position of the engine feet (or lugs) it must be countersunk, as in Fig. 2.5, and covered with a stopper. The best type of bolt for this work is the cut square carriage bolt.

Countersunk bolt heads on the water side should be "stopped" with a suitable compound. However, where a boat repeatedly grounds on a hard bottom the protruding rounded bolt heads need not be let into the wood as they help protect the planking from damage caused by rubbing. If long through bolts cannot be used the bearers may be supported by stringers (Fig. 2.6).

The craft should then be floated in some quiet backwater, first making sure that the hole drilled in the stern for the propeller-shaft stern tube has been plugged to prevent flooding, if the shaft and stern tube are not already in place. In the water the hull should be floating at the water line planned by the designer—that is, the amounts of water drawn fore and aft are in the correct ratio to each other and the vessel is neither down by the head nor the stern and does not have a marked list to port or starboard.

With the hull securely moored, pencil marks are made an equal distance above the water line at the bow and the stern—either from the shore or by

FIG. 2.4. *Allowance must be made for parts of the engine coming below the level of the bearers. These parts may be painted in a different colour, as in the case of this Parsons Scampi. Developing 35 h.p. at 4,000 r.p.m., this petrol engine is a typical unit for small fast craft.*

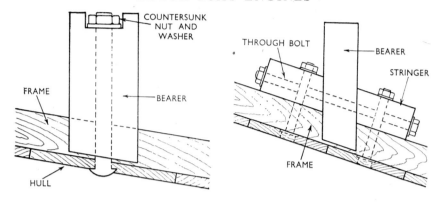

(Left) Fig. 2.5. *Cross section of bearer bolted in position over frame. Note the countersunk nut and protruding bolt head.* (Right) Fig. 2.6. *Where size of bearer precludes the use of bolts directly, it can be supported by stringers as shown.*

someone in waders. Do not let anyone lean over the bow or stern to do the job or the trim of the craft will be severely upset. The engine is next placed aboard and rested on the centre of the bearers. The bow and stern marks are checked, with nobody on board. If the craft has sunk more by the stem than the stern the engine must be dragged a little aft. If it has sunk more by the stern than the stem the engine must be moved forward. This jockeying should be continued until both bow and stern sink by an equal distance and there is no pronounced list to port or starboard.

Port or starboard list can be measured with an ordinary carpenter's or machinist's spirit level placed on the engine top or other flat surface. If a

Fig. 2.7. *Easily manhandled into position on board, the Watermota Seafarer is a twin - cylinder two-stroke petrol engine developing up to 15 b.h.p. at 4,500 r.p.m. The engine is available with reversible pitch propeller and uses the Siba Dynastart generator.*

FIG. 2.8. *Suitable tackle would be necessary for getting an engine of this size on board. The Lister HA 3MGR three-cylinder diesel weighs half a ton, is air-cooled and gives 33 b.h.p. at 1,800 r.p.m.*

clinometer is included in the ship's equipment it can be temporarily screwed over the hull centre line to any convenient bulkhead to indicate the amount of list. Port or starboard list can be corrected by moving the engine in the opposite direction. In a small craft, moving an engine only a fraction of an inch can often correct a list of several degrees.

In a fair-sized craft, provision should also be made for temporary installation of the fuel and water tanks in the hull if these are of large capacity. If possible, they should be placed in the approximate position they will occupy when fitting out is finished. They can be filled with water. This will help to ensure that the engine is mounted over the craft's centre of gravity.

Getting engines like the small Watermota Seafarer (Fig. 2.7) aboard and into position presents no handling problem, but engines like the Lister HA 3MGR (Fig. 2.8) are much too heavy to be manhandled. They can be placed aboard using suitable tackle (as described later) before the craft is launched and lashed into place as a temporary measure to prevent damage when the boat slides down the slipway (which may be at a steep angle) into the water.

In cases where the boat is manhandled into the water and the engine fitted later, it may be required to check the trim of the craft before the power unit is installed. In this event, bags of sand can be used to provide equivalent weight.

The bags can be about 50 lb. in weight. Half a dozen of them are placed between the bearers, side by side, and shifted forward or aft until the correct trim is obtained. The bearers are marked and the engine is then installed over the section occupied by the bags. Sandbags can also be used to represent filled fuel and water tanks when trim tests are under way.

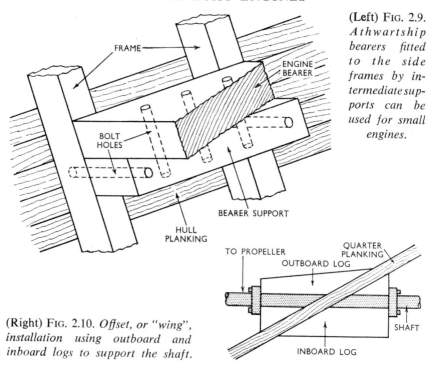

(Left) FIG. 2.9. *Athwartship bearers fitted to the side frames by intermediate supports can be used for small engines.*

(Right) FIG. 2.10. *Offset, or "wing", installation using outboard and inboard logs to support the shaft.*

Small engines can be supported on athwartship or transverse engine bearers (Fig. 2.9). This is popular in sailing craft where the auxiliary engine shaft protrudes through the side of the hull, the arrangement being termed an offset or wing propeller (Fig. 2.10). The same method of aligning is used as for fore-and-aft engine bearers. Athwartship bearers are easy to install but the frame timbers must be sound and preferably sawn from solid timber, not steam bent.

Some single and twin cylinder engines have a tendency to vibrate. To reduce this, transverse timbers, also called floors, can be fitted (Fig. 2.11). Engines can also be mounted between their bearers as shown in Fig. 2.12, and on the floors (Fig. 2.13).

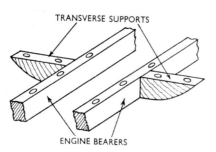

FIG. 2.11. *Vibration can be reduced by fitting bearers with transverse supports bolted to the hull.*

ENGINE INSTALLATION

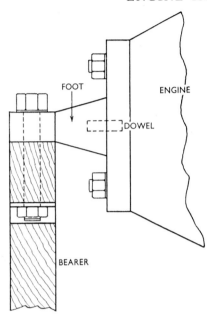

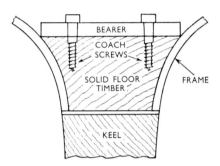

Fig. 2.12. *Engines are sometimes mounted between bearers. Accurate alignment is ensured by the use of a dowel as shown.*

Fig. 2.13. *Bed for an auxiliary engine which has to be installed in a position near the stern.*

PROPELLER SHAFT ALIGNMENT

When the craft is floating evenly with the engine in position the unit should be lightly bolted to the bearers, but not finally secured as it has yet to be aligned to the propeller shaft coupling. The engine may have to be raised or lowered to enable the coupling flanges to match up correctly. The propeller shaft is never aligned to the engine; it is always the engine that is aligned to the shaft. The reason is that the shaft has a very limited amount of play in the stern tube bearings. Once the shaft is inserted in the tube (and this is better done before the hull is launched), no alteration can be made in its position. If it is pulled out of line and forced to match up with the engine, bearing trouble will result when the engine is running.

Propeller shafting is sometimes fitted before the boat is waterborne and the engine installed. This is possible when the exact position the engine is to occupy has already been determined. The engine makers or marine suppliers provide the necessary lengths of shafting and the only remaining job is to line up the engine. Nor is it unusual to launch a craft with the propeller tail shaft in position even when the exact position of the engine is not yet known. The connexion between the tail shaft and the engine flange is made later with an intermediate shaft which can be purchased cut to the required length and fitted with flanges. A kit of parts, with tools, bolts, etc., for installing the Stuart petrol engine shown in the previous chapter, is displayed in Fig. 2.14.

Lining-up the engine is not a difficult job, but demands great care and attention to detail. With the engine in position on the bearers, pilot holes of about ⅛ in. diameter are drilled into the timber to the required depth, which must be equal to the length of the holding bolts or studs. These holes are afterwards enlarged until the bolts or studs can be pushed into place with no more force than that of a light hammer touch. If studs (threaded rods) are used, as is to be recommended, the lower nuts may be welded to steel plates. Holes to accommodate nuts and plates must then be cut into the bearers, as shown in Fig. 2.15. The tightening nut is firmly locked by a third nut.

Occasionally coach screws or lag screws are used to hold small engines in position. This is not the best practice but if such screws are used the threads should be of the buttress type, which hold better. The trouble with coach screws is that after they have been removed once or twice for engine adjustment they may fail to hold in the holes they cut into the timber.

With the engine correctly positioned, the flanges of the engine driving shaft and the propeller shaft should be brought together. If the propeller shaft is too short a longer one must be obtained or an intermediate shaft fitted, as in Chapter 13, Fig. 1. If too long the shaft must be expertly cut and the flange replaced.

More often than not the flanges will just touch at one point, while there will be a considerable space between their surfaces on the opposite side. To correct this, metal shims (thin pieces of brass or other metal) or thin wedges are placed between the bearer top surfaces and the forward feet of the engine if they are touching at the bottom, or under the after feet if the flanges are

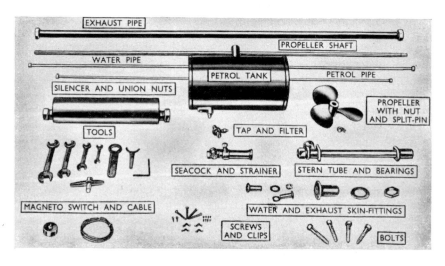

FIG. 2.14. *Complete installation equipment and sterngear as supplied with the Stuart petrol engine shown in Fig. 1.4.*

ENGINE INSTALLATION

(Right) Fig. 2.15. *Engines are best secured by studs, the lower nuts being fitted in recesses cut in the bearers.*

(Below) Fig. 2.16. *Heavy engines may have to be supported on steel sole plates to prevent the feet from digging into the bearer timber.*

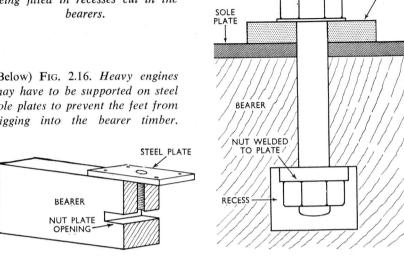

touching at the top. The distance between the flange faces is measured at four points 90 deg. apart with a feeler gauge and metal shim strip is added or removed from beneath the feet until both surfaces are parallel and a 0.003 in. feeler can just be slipped between them. Connecting bolts are inserted and tightened and the bearer bolts pulled up hard.

A final check for correct alignment can be made by slackening back on the flange nuts after the bearer nuts have been tightened fully. If the flanges gape at any point when the nuts are slackened, the shaft has sprung very slightly under the strain of the bolts and the aligning job must be repeated but with greater accuracy.

A newly installed engine does not settle down immediately and the alignment should again be checked after 20 hours' running.

Sometimes when an engine is installed and the holding-down bolts are tightened the engine feet dig into the timber. This can be avoided by resting the feet on steel plates, as in Fig. 2.16. One manufacturer recommends the use of such plates in all installations. They can prevent a great deal of misalignment trouble caused by the engine feet sinking into the wood.

It must also be remembered that a wooden hull alters its shape after it has been afloat for a while. The change is very small but sufficient to interfere with the alignment of engine and shaft. Alignment should be re-checked after the craft has been waterborne for two weeks.

Flexible engine mountings are sometimes used. They are not recommended by all manufacturers, the reason given being that at certain critical speeds excessive vibration may be caused. (Note that all engines have two critical speed ranges, a low and a high. When the engine speed is within either the lower or higher critical speed ranges the result can be a great deal of vibration.) When flexible mountings are used to support the engine a flexible coupling must be placed between the propeller shaft and engine. The use of flexible couplings does not mean that engine and shaft need not be lined up so accurately—the same care must be observed as with rigid couplings.

The use of Fibreglass and other plastic materials for boat hulls does not

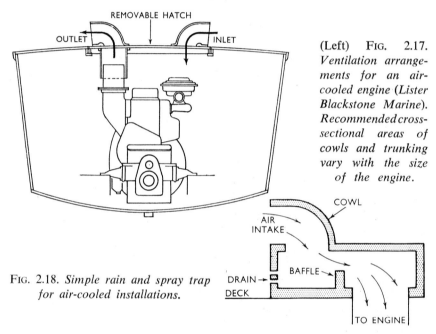

(Left) FIG. 2.17. *Ventilation arrangements for an air-cooled engine (Lister Blackstone Marine). Recommended cross-sectional areas of cowls and trunking vary with the size of the engine.*

FIG. 2.18. *Simple rain and spray trap for air-cooled installations.*

demand any special engine fitting technique. Most of these plastics can be worked with ordinary metal-cutting tools. It is, however, advisable to use longitudinal and not transverse engine bearers with such hulls, as in some cases engine supports attached to the sides of the craft can weaken the structure.

LIFTING THE ENGINE

Small engines can usually be manhandled on to the bearers in the hull, but for the larger ones some sort of lifting rig may have to be improvised. Often it is possible to hire a small mobile crane, or sheer legs can be constructed from lengths of tubular scaffolding or timber. A block and tackle should be used, not a simple sheave, and provision made to secure the tail

ENGINE INSTALLATION

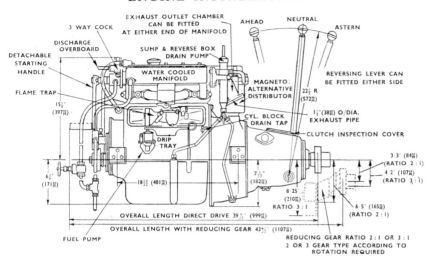

FIG. 2.19. *Manufacturer's installation diagram for the B.M.C. Vedette engine shown below. Much time and trouble can be saved later if such diagrams are carefully studied and the engine space duly laid out before hoisting the engine into position. The Vedette, a four-cylinder petrol unit developing up to 20 b.h.p. at 3,000 r.p.m. offers the advantage of fitting exhaust chamber and gear lever on either side.*

end of the rope to a cleat or bollard to enable the engine to be slowly lowered without danger of it running away and crashing through the hull.

When lifting tackle is not available or cannot be used the engine must be dismantled into as many manageable parts as possible and reassembled on board. Care must be taken to exclude all dirt. Machined and polished surfaces should be wrapped in sacking.

The tackle should be tested for strength before making any heavy lift. It is best to find out from the marine dealer the breaking strain of the rope or wire to be used so that the use of unsuitable tackle will not result in injury or damage. If the weight to be lifted is 200 lb. the breaking strain of the tackle should be 600 lb. at least.

VENTILATION ARRANGEMENTS

When mounting air-cooled engines every effort must be made to ensure that the air supply to the cooling fan and cylinder finning is not interrupted in any way. This type of engine cannot be boxed up in the same way as a water-cooled one. If it is located below deck, trunking must be provided to carry the air to the fan. A very good method is shown in Fig. 2.17. The trunking must be of ample size to supply an abundance of air and at least 10 sq. in. of inlet area must be allowed per horse-power. This means that the trunking for a 10 h.p. air-cooled unit should have a cross-sectional area of 100 sq. in., equal to a square aperture 10 in. by 10 in. If this is not done the engine might be air starved.

After it has cooled the engine surfaces, the ventilating air should leave the engine compartment at a point as far from the intake as possible. This will prevent hot air recirculating.

Spray and heavy rain can be prevented from entering the air ducting by constructing a simple trap, as shown in Fig. 2.18. There are also specially designed ventilators for this job. However, as marine engines are particularly robust, no great damage should result from an occasional splash of spray entering the intake. The engine must, of course, be fitted with an air-intake cleaner to prevent water or dirt being sucked into the cylinders. The fan will whirl into the bilges any water that does enter the engine compartment. The only objection to this is that it has to be pumped out, often manually.

The importance of correct engine mounting and alignment in a boat can hardly be over-emphasised. When in doubt concerning any matter affecting the installation of a particular engine, always contact the maker. Manufacturers can often supply detailed installation drawings for their engines. As an example, Fig. 2.19 is the installation drawing for the engine illustrated. These drawings save time and trouble. They give such information as the length, height and breadth of the unit as well as mounting-bolt hole diameters, position of controls, and other essential details.

CHAPTER 3

Starting and Running the Engine

An efficient power craft is always ready to start at a moment's notice and able to operate for long periods without mechanical interruptions. This state of efficiency is, however, attainable only when a sound operating procedure is followed by the boat owner.

STARTING A PETROL ENGINE

The first essential, of course, is that the engine must have petrol, spark, oil and water (if liquid-cooled). The correct starting procedure is therefore as follows.

1. Check the amount of petrol in the tank. Open all valves and cocks in the piping between the tank and the carburettor. See that the carburettor air-intake screen is clean. The drip tray should be wiped dry.

2. Check the oil level and oil by hand any places not included in the mechanical lubricating system, such as the plummer blocks on the intermediate shaft.

3. Open all valves in the water-cooling circuit.

4. Place the clutch in the neutral position.

5. Open the throttle about one-quarter (this depends on the engine, and detailed instructions are included in the maker's manual) and retard the spark about three-quarters. Failure to retard the spark can result in firing before the piston reaches top centre. This may damage the starting motor or injure the person who hand-cranks the engine if it "kicks back."

When these preliminaries are completed:

1. Turn on the bilge blower (if fitted) and, after three or four minutes, the ignition switch.

2. Press the starter button or crank by hand.

3. As soon as the engine fires, advance the spark—but not so far as to start "knocking"—and regulate the throttle to prevent racing.

4. If the engine is fitted with a dual coil-ignition and magneto system, the ignition should be switched over from the battery to the magneto when the engine has been got going.

5. Keep the engine running at idling speed until it has warmed up and runs smoothly. The engine is now ready to throw in the clutch.

The choke can always be used to assist in starting, but when this is used the throttle should not be opened too wide as it will cause the engine to race. Also, if the carburettor is choked to too great a degree it will flood and the mixture will be too rich to burn. If this happens, push the choke control back against the dashboard and turn over the engine a few times with the ignition switched off before attempting another start.

In very cold weather starting can be assisted by wrapping the carburettor body and intake manifold with rags and pouring boiling water over them. When extremely difficult starting is encountered, the spark plugs can be removed and the smallest drop of petrol squirted into each cylinder. After "rocking" the engine a few times with the crank or starter motor, the ignition should be switched on and the starter pressed. The engine should then fire without trouble. Further information on starting troubles is given in Chapter 4.

When under way the engine requires the following attention:

1. See that the petrol supply from the tank to the carburettor is uninterrupted and that any fuel leaks, however small, are promptly repaired.

2. Advance the spark as far as possible without causing the engine to knock.

3. Make certain that the battery charging rate is not excessive. (See Chapter 8).

4. Maintain the correct amount of oil in the crankcase.

5. Check the cooling water discharge temperature, if possible. If there is a tendency for the temperature of the engine to rise above normal, stop and check the inlet water strainer for blockage.

6. Keep the bilges dry and pump out any collected water.

7. Inspect the shaft gland for excessive leakage. Make sure the shaft is not running hot.

It is not advisable to increase the speed suddenly by quickly opening the throttle wide. The engine gains speed more effectively and suffers less strain when the throttle is gradually opened. Nor should the spark be used to alter engine speed, which should only be done by throttle regulation. An exception is with some very old two-stroke direct-drive engines which can be reversed by means of the spark controls.

Avoid running the craft in shallow water where mud and sand can be stirred up and sucked into the system by the cooling-water pump. This will cause trouble through overheating in direct cooling systems.

If the engine is equipped with a governor this should not be tampered with. Governors are set to give the best possible engine output by the maker, and if re-adjustment should become necessary, this should only be undertaken with full reference to the maker's instructions and using the appropriate tools.

A new engine, or one that has just had a complete overhaul, should be run for at least 10 to 30 hours at reduced speed to permit the moving parts to wear in properly. This is the "running in" period.

It is not advisable to reverse the engine at full speed except in an emergency. When approaching a landing a good seaman stops the engine at some distance from the landing stage, this distance depending on the boat's speed, load, and the state of the tide or current, so that full speed astern is not necessary. Nothing will ruin engine bearings more rapidly than suddenly going full astern. Reverse-gear and reduction-gear teeth also suffer. Of course, in an emergency an engine must be put astern rapidly but only for the shortest possible time.

Never engage the clutch suddenly, as by doing so the clutch and reverse and reduction gear can be unnecessarily strained. Engage it slowly and firmly. Any clutch slippage must be corrected as soon as possible (see Chapter 11).

When stopping the engine follow this procedure :

1. Close the throttle.
2. Place the clutch in neutral.
3. Turn off the ignition.

If the engine is to remain idle for some time or is stopped for the night,

FIG. 3.1. *Electric starting with solenoid control is employed on the Petter PC3 RMR three-cylinder diesel. This engine develops 15 b.h.p. at 3,000 r.p.m.*

close all valves in the petrol system to prevent flooding the bilges in the event of a leak developing. *This is very important.* Also, close all valves in the water inlet circuit.

In cold weather, or when frosty nights are expected, the engine can be wrapped in an old blanket to ensure easy starting in the morning. In very cold weather, when there is the possibility of a freeze-up, the entire engine-cooling system must be drained unless provision can be made to keep it warm enough to prevent freezing and bursting the jackets or pipes. Small engine rooms or engine spaces can be heated with a safety lamp or sump heater. Anti-freeze compounds can be used in closed systems.

Electrical gear, the batteries, starter motor, and dynamo should be separately wrapped if the boat is to lie idle for a few days.

STARTING A DIESEL

Diesel engines have a somewhat different starting procedure. All that is needed to start one in good condition is to place the starting control in the running position, then press the starting button. The engine should fire almost immediately. There are no ignition or carburettor controls, of course.

Fig. 3.2. *Available with either hand or electric starting, the twin-cylinder Enfield 85 diesel is equipped with a starting aid for very cold conditions. A small quantity of commercial ether is placed in the cups connected to the induction system, and the engine then started in the normal way.*

STARTING AND RUNNING THE ENGINE

If a diesel does not fire after a few attempts it is no use pressing the starter button and hoping for the best. The trouble is more than likely to be an air lock in the fuel-injection system, generally caused by leaky fuel lines. In this case, the system should first be hand-primed until fuel that is completely free from air bubbles flows from the top of the fuel filter, i.e. the vent valve or cap. Then, if the engine still does not start, follow this procedure:

1. Place the throttle or governor control in the wide-open or full-speed position.

2. Loosen the fuel-pipe nuts at one of the spray nozzles (injectors).

3. Remove the inspection cover or plate of the fuel pump.

4. Work the pump plunger connected to that nozzle up and down with a screwdriver until clear fuel free from bubbles flows from the pipe (or use the hand priming pump); then tighten the connexion.

5. Repeat this procedure with all the other nozzles. This will bleed all air from the system unless there is something seriously wrong on the suction side of the pump, such as a cracked fuel pipe or leaky filter gasket.

Do not operate the fuel pump with one or more lines closed off, as the high pressure will rupture the pipe. If a pipe has to be disconnected from the spray nozzle for some reason, the fuel should be caught in a container or the line temporarily hooked-up to the surplus return line.

When the engine is running, allow it to idle for a few minutes before leaving the quay and applying the load.

DO'S AND DON'TS: PETROL AND DIESEL

The following operating hints are applicable to all types of engines.

Keep the filters clean; dirty filters cause rapid wear and big maintenance bills.

Keep the fuel oil clean; do not store it in dirty containers.

Keep the lubricating oil clean and drain the crankcase at the end of each period of operation recommended by the manufacturer. It is advisable to use only branded oils.

Do not allow the lubricating oil to fall below the level marked on the dipstick.

Never try to run the engine without oil, or if it is water-cooled, without a supply of water. Engines taken ashore for repair can use a barrel of water as a supply, with inlet and outlet piping led to the barrel, if it is absolutely necessary to test them before returning them to the craft. This method can also be applied to the smaller outboard engines.

Do not allow air cleaners to clog. They protect the engine from undue wear.

The electrolyte in batteries must always be maintained at correct level, otherwise the plates inside will warp and the battery will be ruined.

Do not attempt to start the engine without checking that the propeller is free to revolve and will not tangle with ropes, etc.

Never allow an engine to run without oil pressure showing on the gauge.

Do not allow fuel in the tank to run so low that it may allow the fuel-transfer pump to uncover the bottom of the suction line and so fill the piping with air, which will cause the engine to splutter and stop. Loss of power, erratic running and poor performance of an engine in good mechanical condition can often be traced to this simple fault.

Never run the starting motor for more than 30 seconds at a time. There should then be a rest period of at least one minute before again pressing the starter. Starter motors easily overheat and if not given a short rest can burn out.

Finally, always read the manufacturer's instructions before starting any type of engine.

DAILY INSPECTION

The following inspection should be made daily; it takes only minutes.

1. Check the entire engine, whether diesel or petrol, to make sure that there are no loose bolts, nuts, screws or electrical connexions, and also stop all fuel, oil and water leaks. There will probably be very little tightening needed, but one loose part can often cause serious damage or delay.

2. Remove the filter plugs and drain both fuel and lubricating-oil filters. Petrol filters of the bowl type must also be drained and wiped clean.

3. Inspect and clean the air filter. If this is of the oil-bath type see that the oil reaches its correct working level.

4. Check the level of electrolyte in the batteries and top-up with distilled water if necessary.

5. The water-circulating system should be checked. If of the closed type, top-up the tank to the correct level. Rainwater is better than tap water, which creates lime deposits in the system. Distilled water is better still, however.

FITTING-OUT AFTER LAYING-UP

When an engine has been out of service for some considerable period (see "Laying-Up", page 211), a few precautions should be observed before any attempt is made to start it up again. These are:

1. Drain off any anti-freeze that may have been put into the cooling system and refill with fresh water.

2. Check the whole of the cooling system for signs of leakage; also adjust the water pump packing if required and grease the pump.

3. Remove any seals from the air intake and exhaust pipe.

4. Check the oil levels in the engine sump and gear casing.

5. Check the condition of the battery.

CHAPTER 4

Rapid Trouble Tracing

SUDDEN breakdown or faulty running of a boat's engine can cause much trouble and the loss of a great deal of pleasure to the owner who is not mechanically minded. Unless he knows just what to look for, where to look for it, and what to do when the trouble has been tracked down, he may waste a good deal of time over some quite small fault. Normally, tracing engine faults is comparatively straightforward, even for the novice, but successful and rapid trouble-tracing depends on using a logical system which can be followed step by step until the defect is revealed. Whether the engine is a petrol or diesel, inboard or outboard, air-cooled or water-cooled, this systematic trouble-finding procedure is essential.

This chapter sets out a fault-tracing procedure that can be used whenever an engine refuses to start or will not run properly. It does not deal with major repairs, which are covered elsewhere in this book, but outlines the more common causes of engine troubles.

PETROL ENGINES: FAULTY STARTING

In practically every case of an engine refusing to start, or when it suddenly stops, the fault will be found in either the fuel or ignition systems. The first thing to do in such cases, therefore, is to find out which of these systems is at fault. The following procedure can be followed.

First, check that there is adequate petrol in the fuel tank. Then, with the ignition "off", try the starter. If the engine cranks easily when the button is pressed the battery must be in good condition. If not, a discharged battery may be the sole cause of the trouble.

Next, switch on the ignition and again crank the engine. Watch the ammeter needle. If it swings over to the "discharge" section of its dial, current is flowing through the ignition coil. To check this further, disconnect a lead from any of the sparking plugs and hold the bared end about $\frac{1}{4}$ in. to $\frac{3}{8}$ in. away from the cylinder head while someone else switches on the ignition and cranks the engine. While you are making this test, take care to keep the fingers well clear of the bared cable end or you may receive a nasty shock. If a strong white spark snaps across the space between the lead and the cylinder-block metal, this proves that ignition current is available from the

49

distributor. Remove the spark plug, reconnect the lead to it and lay the plug on top of the engine. When the engine is cranked again, you should see a spark between the plug points. Check the other plugs in the same way, one by one. If no spark can be obtained at a plug, either that plug or its connecting cable is likely to be at fault.

If all plugs appear to be firing normally, the fuel system should next be checked. First, however, make certain that no one in the boat is smoking or using a stove or anything else with a naked flame. *Never take risks with petrol.*

Remove the petrol tank filler cap and recheck the contents of the tank. Often a mere puddle in the bottom may appear at first glance to be several inches of fuel, so test with a dipstick. Turn off the petrol tap or valve at the tank bottom and remove the petrol strainer or filter bowl. If this is clogged with dirt or sediment it should be cleaned and then refitted.

Make certain that the carburettor adjustments have not been changed. See also that the choke cable is not loose at the carburettor end and that the choke control is functioning correctly. If these parts are all in order, check that fuel is actually reaching the carburettor by turning off the petrol tap at the tank bottom, then loosening the petrol pipe at the carburettor. Turn on the tap again. With a gravity-feed system petrol should flow from the loosened connexion unless the tank or supply line is obstructed. When a fuel pump is installed, switch on the ignition and crank the engine. If the fuel line is clear and the pump is working, petrol should now flow from the loose connexion. Trouble in the pump itself can often be traced to a worn diaphragm or leaky valves, or to a clogged filter if the pump incorporates one.

Before trying to start the engine again all traces of petrol must be wiped up and the rags disposed of, otherwise petrol fumes can linger in the bilges, with the risk of causing an explosion.

So far we have assumed that the electric starter is working normally and will crank the engine. If it will not do so, however, a check should be made as follows:

1. Make certain that the clutch is disengaged.

2. Check whether the battery is charged by means of a hydrometer test (see Chapter 9).

3. Check the battery cables; all connexions must be tight, not broken, frayed, corroded or wet.

4. Try turning the engine by hand. If it cannot be turned over but will rock gently when the starting handle is released, remove the spark plugs and examine all cylinders for the presence of water. Water can enter through open exhaust valves in some types of water-cooled exhaust installations and under certain conditions, and also through a cracked exhaust manifold, cylinder head or cylinder block.

If the battery is almost discharged it may still be possible to start by hand-cranking the engine. To do this, turn on the ignition and operate the choke and throttle in the usual manner, but do *not* use the starter motor. If the engine can be turned over by hand but will not start, check the following:

1. See that the ignition switch is turned on.

2. Make sure the ignition wiring, H.T. coil, distributor cap and spark plugs are dry. If not, dry each part carefully, and pay particular attention to the inside of the distributor cap. Be careful not to change the order of the connexions to the plugs.

3. Examine the wiring for breaks or faulty connexions.

4. Inspect the contact-breaker points (see page 131). They may be dirty, worn or pitted, and either need cleaning up or replacement by a new set. If the contact points are severely pitted the condenser is possibly defective, in which case it should be replaced by a new one.

5. Check the contact-breaker movable arm. It may be sticking or have its spring broken. Replace any defective parts, and clean and lubricate the arm if it is sticking.

6. Remove the distributor cap and watch the contact-breaker points move as the engine is hand-cranked or turned over by pulling on the flywheel. At the setting where the points are farthest apart, carefully measure the distance between them by means of a feeler gauge, then compare this measurement with the maker's recommendation. If the contact-breaker gap is not precisely correct it must be adjusted.

7. Inspect the fuel system, as described above.

PETROL ENGINES: FAULTY RUNNING

The commonest troubles encountered when the engine is actually running are misfiring or uneven running, backfiring, "knocking" or "pinking", unusual noises, excessive vibration, and loss of power. The following checks will help to identify the causes of such troubles.

Regular Misfiring. When an engine misfires and the "missing" is regular it is a clear indication that the trouble is in one cylinder only, or two at the most. To locate the faulty cylinder, take a screwdriver with an insulated handle and short-circuit each sparking plug in turn while the engine is running. The blade of the screwdriver should be pressed firmly against the cylinder head and the metal shank brought into contact with the sparking plug terminal or the bared ignition cable. This "earths" the supply of current to that particular plug and so short-circuits it.

If the result is that the engine speed falls off even a little, then it can be taken that the cylinder tested is functioning normally. The test should be repeated with other cylinders until one is found where short circuiting the plug makes no difference to engine speed: this will be the faulty one. *Note: Be careful to hold the screwdriver only by its insulated handle when testing in this way. If the metal part is touched, a shock may result from the high-voltage ignition system.*

The usual causes of regular misfiring are:

1. The ignition cable to one of the plugs is not properly connected; or it may be broken, frayed or have its insulation damaged.

2. The sparking plug is in poor condition, either because it is wet, or the porcelain is cracked, or the points are dirty. If wet, thoroughly dry the plug, clean and replace. If damaged or badly fouled, it is best to fit a new plug.

3. Leaky valves. A valve may leak because it is sticking, because its contact surface is burned, or because the valve spring is weak or broken. One quick test is to crank the engine by hand and note the feeling of resistance due to the compression of each cylinder when both its valves are closed and the piston is rising towards the top of its compression stroke. There will be less resistance to the starting handle if a cylinder has a leaky valve.

4. Leaky cylinder-head gasket. This is usually revealed by the loud noise which comes from the fractured area of the gasket or by discoloration of the paintwork around this area. Sometimes the leak can be actually seen or felt.

5. Cracked cylinder head. This is unlikely unless the engine has been operated without a sufficient supply of cooling water, or the holding-down nuts or bolts in the head have been overtightened, or the head has been mishandled during an overhaul. Cracks on the underside of the head are usually found in the area of the valve apertures, especially in overhead valve engines.

6. Fractured distributor cap. Again, this is a rare fault, but it can happen and lead to earthing of the ignition current, so that one or more cylinders are short-circuited.

Irregular Misfiring. If the misfiring is intermittent instead of regular, the cause is probably one of the following:

1. Over-rich fuel mixture caused by flooding of the carburettor or leaving the choke control in operation after the engine has started.

2. Loose or damaged ignition wiring. Vibration will sometimes interfere with a wiring connexion or contact, leading to momentary misfiring. When the irregularity persists, all wiring must be checked for damaged cable insulation which may cause short circuits as the bare wire touches engine metal.

3. Contact-breaker arm sticking and then breaking loose, possibly due to a weak spring.

4. Valves sticking, then breaking loose. This is often due to carbon adhering to the valve stems and can be reduced, if not cured, by squirting just a few drops of paraffin oil on to the stem of the valve affected.

5. Defective H.T. coil. This is not a frequent trouble; it can only be remedied by fitting a new coil.

Backfiring. This unmistakable noise can occur either in the carburettor or in the exhaust pipe or silencer. If it occurs in the carburettor the cause is a flame in the cylinder when an intake valve opens to admit a further charge of the petrol-air mixture. When it takes place in the exhaust pipe or silencer it is usually due to unburnt fuel from a misfiring cylinder getting into the system and being ignited by hot exhaust gases.

Carburettor backfiring can also be due to:

1. Fuel mixture too "lean" (i.e. contains insufficient petrol). This can be temporarily cured by more use of the choke control. Sometimes the control screws of the carburettor have been incorrectly set, and must be readjusted according to the maker's instructions. Another cause of insufficient petrol in the mixture is the presence of water or dirt in the fuel supply, preventing the free flow of petrol through the filters.

2. If the fuel supply is low, the petrol pipe at the point where it connects with the tank may not be completely submerged. When this happens insufficient petrol will be delivered to the carburettor to maintain normal running of the engine. The same thing can result from a blockage of the petrol tank vent, which will hinder the free flow of fuel and possibly prevent any petrol reaching the carburettor.

When the backfiring is in the exhaust pipe look for these faults:

1. The cable leading to one of the spark plugs is broken or has become disconnected.

2. One of the spark plugs is either very dirty or its current is short-circuiting to the engine metal owing to the porcelain insulator getting wet.

3. An exhaust valve is sticking in the open position.

Engine Knocks. Engine knocking, pinking or pinging, a metallic noise resembling hammering on an anvil—especially if it is irregular and is more pronounced when the engine is accelerated suddenly—is generally due to fuel detonation or pre-ignition. Here are likely causes:

1. The ignition timing is too far advanced and needs retarding.

2. The fuel mixture is too lean and the carburettor controls must be readjusted in accordance with the maker's recommendation.

3. Considerable carbon has accumulated on the crowns of the pistons, the valves, and the underside of the cylinder heads. The engine needs decarbonising.

4. The engine may be overheating because there is insufficient water circulating through the jackets. Or, if air-cooled, the flow of air to the cylinder finning has been interrupted, either because of a blockage in the air trunking leading to the engine or because of fan failure.

5. The wrong type of spark plug is fitted. Refer to the engine maker's handbook for the correct type of plug to be used with the power unit.

6. The petrol in use is of too low a grade.

Engine Noises and Vibration. A pounding noise is an indication of loose, damaged, or badly worn parts. Causes can be:

1. Bent propeller shaft, damaged propeller blades, or propeller loose on its shaft.

2. Worn propeller shaft bearing (on outboard engines).

3. Engine not firmly secured to its bed; it must be re-aligned to the shaft and tightened down.

4. Valves are sticking in the open position.

5. Worn crankshaft bearing. In this case the pounding will be more pronounced when the engine is rapidly accelerated or suddenly slowed down.

6. Worn connecting-rod bottom end ("big end") bearings. The noise in this case may be more of a clatter than a pounding. If the trouble appears to be present in one cylinder only then the bottom end bearing concerned may be burned out through failure of the lubricating oil supply.

Heavy vibration can be caused when the engine is not firmly secured to its bed. A bent propeller shaft, a lost propeller, and a chipped propeller blade will all produce similar vibration.

Low Oil Pressure. If the oil pressure gauge shows abnormally low reading (or no pressure at all) the engine must be stopped at once and the cause ascertained, otherwise serious damage can result. Likely causes of low oil pressure and their remedies are:

1. There is insufficient oil in the engine oil sump—top up with fresh oil to the correct level.

2. The oil is badly diluted—drain the sump and refill with clean oil.

3. The oil is overheated due to trouble in the oil cooling system or because the engine, if water-cooled, is not receiving sufficient coolant. This condition will also be indicated by the presence of smoke coming from the oil filler cap or crankcase breather.

4. The oil cooler is leaking—check for oil in the bilges.

5. The wrong grade of oil is being used—refer to the engine maker's handbook for the correct grade.

6. The oil cooler, if fitted, is not receiving sufficient water due to obstruction of the cooling tubes—clean out any marine weeds, sand or mud sucked into the system.

Engine Lacks Power. If the engine seems unable to develop normal power and the speed of the boat is reduced, the following possible causes of trouble should be considered.

1. The hull is fouled with marine growths, barnacles, slime, etc.

2. The propeller or its strut is fouled by weeds, rope, etc.

3. The propeller or its shaft, or both, are damaged.

4. The ignition timing is too far retarded and must be reset to the engine maker's specification.

5. The carburettor needs cleaning or readjusting.

6. The compression is too low and the cylinders, pistons and rings need overhaul.

7. The valves are incorrectly adjusted. All tappet clearances should be measured and, if necessary, reset to the engine maker's specification.

8. The grade of petrol in use is unsuitable to the engine.

DIESEL ENGINES: FAULTY STARTING

Diesel engines are liable to many of the troubles already mentioned as applicable to petrol engines. In addition, there are certain troubles which are peculiar to this type of power unit. If the diesel will not start, or starts only with difficulty, the reason may be one of the following:

1. Insufficient fuel—check the tank.

2. If the engine has not been used for some time the fuel system needs to be primed by operating the hand pump.

3. Batteries are too weak to turn the engine over.

4. Wrong type of fuel is being used.

5. Water is present in the fuel due to condensation in tank (see Chapter 10, Outboard and Jet Engines).

6. Piston rings or cylinders are badly worn and compression is low.

7. Inlet or exhaust valves are leaking.

8. The cylinder head gasket is leaking.

9. The air intake cleaner is choked and needs cleaning.

10. The governor control lever is in the stop position.

DIESEL ENGINES: FAULTY RUNNING

If the engine can be started but stops without warning, the following should be checked:

1. Fuel supply exhausted. Refill tank and prime the system before attempting to start again.

2. Fuel pumps or fuel strainers or filters are air-bound and need priming.

3. The fuel line is obstructed or broken.

4. Fuel transfer pump (if fitted) is not operating.

5. Water is present in the fuel.

6. Piston seizure due to lack of lubrication; this trouble would be preceded by unusual noises from the engine.

7. Fuel pump needs retiming (see Chapter 8, Diesel Fuel Pumps).

8. Bearings have seized up due to lack of lubrication; this would be preceded by a heavy pounding noise.

Misfiring. If the engine misfires or fires erratically on all cylinders, check the following:

1. Wrong grade of fuel—drain and refill tank with correct grade fuel.

2. Water present in the fuel—drain off the supply and settle-out or centrifuge before returning to tank, or refill with clean fuel.

3. Sticking nozzle valve stems, or pump delivery valves, or pump plunger (even a combination of all three might occur) in the fuel injection pump. In the event of these troubles all parts would have to be removed and cleaned, a job demanding considerable care which is best done by an expert.

4. Worn piston rings or cylinders, or both. This normally occurs only after the engine has been in service for many years, but can be accelerated if the engine is misused.

5. Inlet or exhaust valves are leaking.

6. The air cleaner is choked and needs cleaning.

7. In the case of a two-stroke engine, the compressor drive may be broken or needs adjusting.

If a diesel misfires in one or two cylinders, the following procedure should be adopted. First locate the "missing" cylinder, using much the same method as described for petrol engines with the difference that instead of disconnecting spark-plug cables, fuel oil pipes are slackened back. Loosen the connexion holding the fuel tubing to the spray nozzles one at a time, allowing fuel to spill from the connexion instead of being pumped to the spray nozzle. If the engine speed drops when this is done to a spray nozzle, the cylinder concerned is firing normally. If the engine speed remains unaffected, then that cylinder is "missing". Likely causes of the trouble are :

1. Fuel valve of the spray nozzle is stuck in its body. It must be removed and cleaned or replaced.

2. Air is present in the fuel line, in which case the system must be "bled" in accordance with instructions in the maker's handbook.

3. Exhaust or inlet valve sticking. As noted earlier, it is sometimes possible to free a valve by squirting a *few* drops of paraffin oil on to the stem, otherwise dismantling is necessary.

4. Leaky exhaust or intake valve, or valve spring weakened or broken.

5. Incorrect valve adjustment. Reset tappet clearances in accordance with the maker's specification.

6. Fuel pump delivery valve leaking or sticking. The complete delivery valve assembly must be lifted out of the pump and cleaned or replaced.

7. Fuel pump delivery valve spring broken. The complete unit must be replaced.

8. Worn piston rings or cylinders, or both.

Dirty or Smoky Exhaust. This condition can be very offensive to others and should not be neglected. It arises when combustion of the fuel inside the cylinders is not complete. The exhaust gases will then be brown, or even black, in colour, depending on the amount of unburned carbon present. A smoky exhaust does not necessarily indicate any serious derangement; a few adjustments to the injection system may be all that is required. Here are some causes of this trouble:

1. Valves are leaking and need regrinding.

2. The wrong type of fuel is being used.

3. The spray valves need cleaning or adjusting. They may be "dribbling"; that is, small drops of oil are entering the cylinder before the correct injection moment.

4. Fuel injection is taking place too early and requires adjusting. This condition will be accompanied by a "fuel knock".

5. Piston rings are worn and need renewing.

6. The fuel delivery valves in the pump need cleaning, or one of them is broken.

7. Fuel pump needs retiming (see Chapter 8, Diesel Fuel Pumps).

If the exhaust smoke gradually gets darker over a considerable period at the same time the consumption of lubricating oil gradually increases, the cause will be wear on the piston rings. Surplus lubricating oil on the cylinder walls is therefore able to pass the pistons and enter the combustion spaces.

Fuel Knocks in Engine. This sound may emanate from one or more cylinders. Should it be in one cylinder only, the possible causes are:

1. The spray valve is sticking and must be removed and cleaned to free it, or the spring which operates it is broken and needs replacing.

2. The fuel valve in the pump unit is sticking or broken.

3. Inlet or exhaust valves are sticking or not seating correctly.

4. The cylinder-head gasket has developed a leak.

When the sound comes from more than one cylinder and is erratic and intermittent, likely causes are:

1. The engine is using the wrong type of fuel.

2. The fuel is dirty and causing more than one valve to stick. All parts of the fuel system should be cleaned thoroughly and all fuel strainers and filters overhauled or replaced.

3. Water is present in the fuel. This is often due to failure to drain the filter sumps regularly and top-up the tank nightly to exclude damp air.

Occasionally the "knocking" is continuous and the exhaust is very black. The trouble is then most probably due to the use of the wrong fuel. If the sound is mechanical and harsh in character, some probable causes, all of which need immediate attention, are:

1. The piston is hitting the inlet or exhaust valves.

2. Valve tappet clearances are not correct.

3. Crankshaft bearings are badly worn—either the main or the connecting rod bottom end ("big end") bearings or both.

4. Pistons, cylinder liners, piston rings, gudgeon pins need replacing.

5. The flywheel may be loose.

CHAPTER 5

Engine Lubrication

THE oil supply for most petrol (except two-stroke) and diesel engines is contained in the sump or oil pan—the container at the base of the engine, which is usually bolted up to the crankcase. The oil drains back into the sump after lubricating the crankshaft bearings, connecting rods, piston rings (and in some cases the pistons), piston or gudgeon pins, the walls of the cylinders, the timing gear, camshaft, valves, and other moving parts. The oil is circulated through the engine by means of a small gear-type or plunger pump, driven by the engine. Two-stroke petrol engines are usually lubricated by oil mixed with the fuel.

Unless a sufficient quantity of oil of the correct type is supplied to the bearings the surrounding metal will soon begin to overheat and eventually the engine will seize up. This means that the metal in a bearing melts and fuses on to the moving component, so that the engine is forcibly stopped and serious damage may be done. The oil therefore must help to remove unwanted heat from moving parts, and some marine engines are fitted with oil coolers which extract much of the heat absorbed by the oil as it travels through the engine.

Fig. 5.1 shows how the oil is circulated in a diesel engine, similar arrangements being used on most petrol engines. The

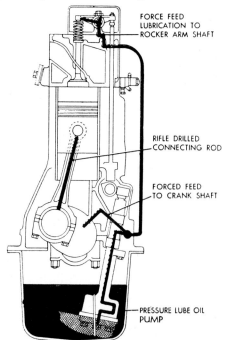

FORCE FEED LUBRICATION TO ROCKER ARM SHAFT

RIFLE DRILLED CONNECTING ROD

FORCED FEED TO CRANK SHAFT

PRESSURE LUBE OIL PUMP

FIG. 5.1. *Oil circulation in a diesel engine, as shown by the heavy line.*

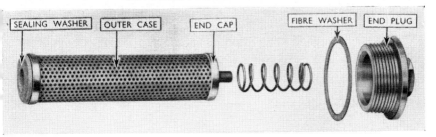

FIG. 5.2. *Oil sump strainer for Enfield diesel engine. The filter element is automatically by-passed if it becomes choked.*

system illustrated is of the forced lubrication type, in which the oil is pumped to the different engine components. In some engines "splash" lubrication is used for the cylinder walls, piston pins and piston rings. In this case the connecting rod bearing cap passes through the sump oil at the end of each stroke and splashes it against the cylinder walls.

The service life of an engine depends largely on the cleanliness of the lubricating oil in use. If this is contaminated by particles of dirt, grit, bearing metal, foundry dross or other impurities, then damage will soon result to the bearings, piston rings and other moving parts. To prevent this happening, the particles of foreign matter are removed by straining the oil through a wiremesh guard placed over the suction point of the oil pump (Fig. 5.2). Then, in most engines, the further precaution is taken of forcing the oil through a filter which removes any remaining particles entrained with the oil.

Oil also becomes contaminated because dirt and water can enter the system through the crankcase filler and the air intake. Even if filters fitted at these points are 95 per cent efficient, a test showed that it is possible for several pounds of dirt to be sucked into the engine during 1,000 hours of running. It has also been proved that two-thirds of all wear in an internal combustion engine is caused by contaminated oil. It will be seen from this that it is essential to have an efficient oil filter fitted, and to clean or renew the element in it at the proper intervals. With most modern engine filter units, the element should be scrapped and a new one fitted at running intervals of somewhere between 200 and 400 hours. A typical filter unit is shown sectioned in Fig. 5.3, and an exploded view of another in Fig. 5.4.

The running period between filter changes varies according to the type of engine and its mechanical condition. With an engine in good mechanical condition the oil is less likely to become contaminated by carbon, formed by combustion gases, which is blown past the rings—as can happen with a worn engine. Again, an engine which is installed in a craft working off shore will

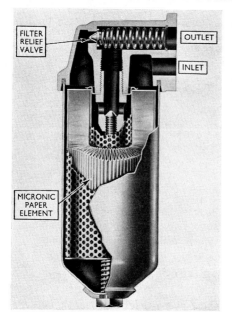

FILTER RELIEF VALVE

OUTLET

INLET

MICRONIC PAPER ELEMENT

PRESSURE RELIEF VALVE

RENEWABLE ELEMENT

FIGS. 5.3 and 5.4. *Lubricating oil filters. The Purolator Full Flow is shown in section* (left) *and an A.C. unit* (right). *Both types use renewable elements and incorporate pressure relief valves.*

not have to deal with such dirty atmospheric conditions as one which uses waterways in the vicinity of industrial areas, where the atmosphere may contain much dust and dirt. There is thus no hard-and-fast rule, but manufacturers always give explicit instructions on filter changing and their advice should be closely followed.

Modern lubricating oils usually have additives of a detergent nature which prevent the formation of sludge which can block up the oil pipes, cause piston rings to stick, and otherwise interfere with the proper functioning of the lubricating system.

Sludge is formed in the oil mainly as a result of inefficient combustion of the fuel. This can occur particularly when the engine is constantly operated at too low a temperature. It can also arise through water leaking into the lubrication system from defective gaskets, or even from a water-cooled exhaust pipe if this has not been properly installed. Some oils also have a tendency to "sludge up" if they are used at temperatures higher than those recommended for the engine by the maker. The factors which tend to bring about sludge formation in an engine also encourage sticking of the piston rings and the formation of lacquer on pistons and cylinder walls. The use of lubricating oils which contain a detergent additive will check this. The presence of sulphur (particularly in diesel fuel oils) will also contribute to fouling of the engine; its effect can be greatly reduced if not eliminated altogether by using detergent-type lubricants. The use of this type of oil is therefore strongly recommended.

LOW OIL PRESSURE

When the oil-pressure gauge indicates that pressure has dropped below that specified for the engine, prompt action must be taken to establish the cause. First, of course, it is as well to check that the gauge itself is in good working order. The best way to do this is to replace it temporarily by another gauge known to be working properly, and compare the readings. Assuming that the gauge is in order, the next thing is to check the amount of oil in the sump, topping it up to the normal working level if necessary. Remember that when oil has been drained from the engine, after refilling to the "full" mark the oil level may drop considerably when the engine is started and the galleries, piping and filters fill up. The dipstick should therefore be inspected after the engine has run for a few minutes and more oil added to make good the "loss".

Wrong Grade of Oil: If the grade of lubricating oil in use is not suitable for the engine the pressure gauge readings may vary from normal. The correct grade, as specified by the engine maker, should always be used. Oils that are too thick and heavy will not reach all the vital points in the lubrication system, and may make starting difficult. On the other hand, oils that are excessively thin or light may not possess the "body" required to ensure adequate lubrication of the moving parts under hot and strenuous conditions.

Fuel Mixed with Lubricating Oil: If the pistons, piston rings or cylinder bores in an engine are badly worn, the diesel fuel or petrol which enters the cylinders may blow past the rings and enter the crankcase, to mix with the lubricating oil. When this is suspected a test can be made by sniffing the sump dipstick—the smell of diesel fuel or petrol will be clearly apparent. This dilution of the oil may result in a lower gauge reading. Correcting the trouble calls for an overhaul; the fitting of new rings may be sufficient, depending on the state of wear, of course. Another symptom of this trouble, strange though it may seem, is that the engine appears not to be using as much lubricating oil as previously! This is because dilution by the fuel is maintaining the oil level on the dipstick despite the engine being in use. The entrance of water into the crankcase through a leaky cylinder-head gasket will have a similar result in maintaining the sump oil level, to the detriment of the engine. Dribbling of the spray nozzles is another cause of fuel oil entering the crankcase in diesel engines.

Worn Bearings: Another cause of abnormally low oil pressure can be wear in the bearings of the engine, particularly if the connecting rod bottom end bearings are worn. Much of the oil pumped to the engine's working parts will then escape past the worn bearing metal back to the sump, and pressure will be reduced.

Relief Valves: Lubrication systems are generally fitted with relief valves which prevent the oil pressure from exceeding the specified figure. If, for any reason, the pressure is raised above normal the relief valve automatically opens, reducing the pressure and allowing surplus oil to escape (Fig. 5.5). However, should this valve open and then fail to close properly the oil pressure will drop, and this can lead to oil starvation in the upper part of the engine. The engine should be stopped at once and the relief valve checked. Its spring may have broken; its setting may have altered because

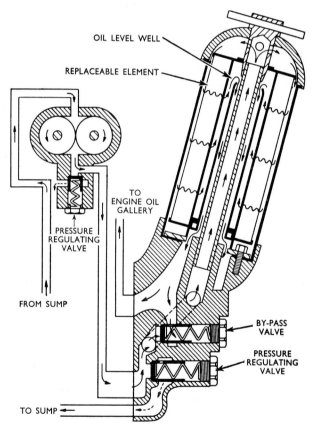

FIG. 5.5. *A typical lubricating oil filter circuit, showing positions of pressure regulating and by-pass valves in relation to the filter element.*

FIG. 5.6. *Crankshaft-driven gear-type oil pump for Enfield diesel engine. Similar units are used in petrol engines.*

DRIVING PINION

| BACKING PLATE | DRIVING GEAR | DRIVEN GEAR | DELIVERY COUPLING |

the adjusting screw has slackened back; or there may be a trace of dirt preventing its seating properly.

There are few oil pipes in the modern engine, oil being carried to the different parts through passages drilled or cast into the engine block, but any such pipes must be checked for leakage when low oil pressure is registered.

If the lubrication system is allowed to get into a very dirty condition the wire-mesh strainer attached to the suction pump which works submerged in the sump sometimes becomes badly clogged. If the cause of the clogging is a film of carbon, this is an indication that the piston rings (and possibly the cylinders) are worn, as it is due to gas blowing by from the upper part of the cylinders.

Very rarely an oil pump fails because of some mechanical fault such as fracture of the drive shaft or failure of a gear pin. Normally they are most reliable, but even though these pumps work continuously in oil they are liable to wear after years of use. If oil pressure gradually drops after a long period of use and all other parts of the system are known to be in good condition, the pump should be taken down and examined for wear. Gear pumps are of simple construction (Fig. 5.6) and a new pump can easily be fitted or the worn parts replaced, as necessary.

HIGH OIL PRESSURE

Occasionally the oil pressure may exceed the figure specified by the engine maker. This can happen, for example, when the relief valve fails to open. All the oil must then pass through the filter, and if the element is dirty and tends to obstruct the flow of oil, pressure in the system will quickly build up. The trouble is easily corrected by cleaning and freeing the relief valve, replacing it if damaged, or re-setting the valve to open at the correct pressure.

Heavy oil which is sludge-laden can also force up the pressure. The solution in this case is to drain the dirty oil, flush out the system and then refill with clean lubricant of the recommended grade.

Flushing out the system calls for the use of a hand pump to force a cleaning fluid such as paraffin oil or carbon tetrachloride through the pipes and passages. At the same time the sump should be taken down and cleaned thoroughly. All sludge sticking to surfaces inside the sump or crankcase must be wiped off. A better job can be ensured by using one of the special flushing oils or compounds that are available. After draining the dirty oil, the sump is filled up with flushing oil and the engine run for some minutes. Then the flushing oil is drained, carrying with it every trace of dirt and sludge, and the fresh lubricant is poured in.

The oil supply in the crankcase should be topped-up daily if necessary to maintain the level at the "Full" dipstick mark. Over-filling should, however, be avoided. If this happens, the connecting rods will dip into the oil and splash an excessive amount on to the cylinder walls. This will cause smoking, excessive carbon build-up, fouled sparking plugs, and sticking valves.

When oil consumption gradually becomes excessive and there are no signs of external oil leaks around the engine, a possible cause is worn piston rings. Rings which are worn fail to prevent the lubricating oil getting past the pistons into the combustion spaces, where the oil is burned with the fuel. This is usually accompanied by a bluish-white exhaust smoke. Wear in the cylinder will result in the same condition.

Oil can also be lost from the oil cooler if there is a leak between the oil side and the raw water on the cooling side. Oil circulates at a higher pressure than the water and if there is a leak it will therefore be forced into the cooling system. Leakage of oil from the cooler will be shown by an oil slick on the surface of the water when the craft is tied up alongside with the engine running. The slick will gradually extend over the surface from the point where the cooling water is discharged overboard.

When an oil cooler is fitted it should be cleaned out at the same time as the lubricating system.

CHAPTER 6

Power Unit Maintenance

In this chapter we shall deal with troubles that may arise inside the power unit, i.e. in connexion with the cylinders, cylinder head, pistons, connecting rods, valve gear, crankshaft, camshaft, bearings and timing gear. Much of the testing and overhaul work described in the following pages can only be carried out by skilled mechanics and fitters having suitable equipment, but the non-expert boat owner may find it of interest to learn what engine overhaul entails. Apart from this, the chapter will show him how to diagnose troubles in the power unit before they become too serious. Fig. 6.1 shows the general construction of a typical overhead-valve petrol engine, in which the components treated in detail later can be identified; while Fig. 6.2 gives sectional views of a popular marine diesel unit.

CYLINDERS

The cylinder bore may be simply an accurate and highly polished hole in the engine block, or it may take the form of a steel sleeve called a "liner" which is fitted into a hole in the block. Most petrol engines are of the former type, whereas most diesels have liners.

In the course of lengthy running, wear occurs in the cylinder which results in its being no longer perfectly round and having walls which are no longer perfectly parallel, but slightly tapered. The ordinary type of cylinder must then be reconditioned by reboring or honing, resulting in an accurate but slightly larger bore into which a larger piston must be fitted. Where liners are used, the worn liner can be extracted and a new one fitted. This has the advantage that the same size piston can still be used, so that the performance characteristics of the engine remain unaffected. Also, the liner can be made of special alloys which have much greater wear resistance than the ordinary engine-block metal.

Cylinder liners are of two types. Those that come into direct contact with the cooling water circulating inside the engine block are called "wet" liners. Those that fit into a bored hole in the block (like an ordinary cylinder bore) and do not make contact with the coolant are called "dry" liners. Both types are illustrated in Fig. 6.3.

Occasionally cylinders and/or liners crack, this trouble being indicated

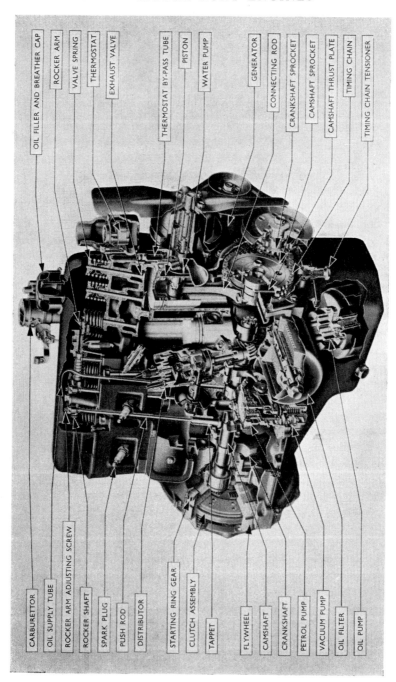

OIL FILLER AND BREATHER CAP

ROCKER ARM

VALVE SPRING

THERMOSTAT

EXHAUST VALVE

THERMOSTAT BY-PASS TUBE

PISTON

WATER PUMP

GENERATOR

CONNECTING ROD

CRANKSHAFT SPROCKET

CAMSHAFT SPROCKET

CAMSHAFT THRUST PLATE

TIMING CHAIN

TIMING CHAIN TENSIONER

CARBURETTOR

OIL SUPPLY TUBE

ROCKER ARM ADJUSTING SCREW

ROCKER SHAFT

SPARK PLUG

PUSH ROD

DISTRIBUTOR

STARTING RING GEAR

CLUTCH ASSEMBLY

TAPPET

FLYWHEEL

CAMSHAFT

CRANKSHAFT

PETROL PUMP

VACUUM PUMP

OIL FILTER

OIL PUMP

FIG. 6.1. *General construction of a typical overhead-valve petrol engine. This is the Ford Consul, widely used for fast craft in its marinized form (Parsons Sea Consul, Watermota Sea Otter, Fenn & Wood FW460, Wortham Blake Sprite). Power output is 55-60 b.h.p. at 4,000 r.p.m.*

by water appearing in the lubricating oil and water collecting in the cylinder when the engine is stopped. Fracturing of the metal can be due to:

1. Inefficient cooling. If the cylinders are not properly cooled they will be unevenly heated and the stresses caused result in cracking. Uneven heating can be caused by scale collecting on the walls of the cooling water passages, by using insufficient water, or by adding cold water to an overheated engine.

2. Poorly fitted pistons. When the clearance between the piston and the liner is too great the result is piston slap, and this subjects the piston and liner to shock blows that lead to breakage.

3. Corrosion. Although a rare event, it is possible for a liner to fail through corrosion which has been set up when the engine is stored for the winter months without the protection of a surface film of oil or grease.

Cracked or broken cylinders in the smaller marine engines must be renewed, as wholly satisfactory repairs cannot be made to them.

Scored Cylinders. The scoring of cylinders is a much more frequent occurrence than breakage. It may make its presence known through sluggish performance or difficult starting because of reduced compression, and is often accompanied by unusually rapid wear of the piston rings. The marks on the cylinder walls will be visible when the cylinder head is lifted and the pistons are set to the bottom of their strokes. They can take the form of deep or shallow scratches running the full length of the piston stroke. In many cases there are also corresponding scratches on the piston and the piston rings.

This scoring or scratching is caused by gritty particles drawn into the cylinders with the intake air. Even small particles of hard material which are not blown out with the exhaust gases can adhere to the walls and cause considerable damage. This indicates the importance of maintaining the air cleaner in proper working condition to filter out dust and dirt in the intake air. Broken piston rings will also cause scoring, and dirty oil is another cause.

Scored cylinders and liners can be reclaimed by reboring to the next largest size and fitting larger pistons. If the marking is slight it can be removed by honing. Occasionally bumps are formed and these can be removed with a hand stone damped in paraffin oil.

Worn and Clogged Ports. In two-stroke engines the ports sometimes wear ragged, and this can lead to piston ring damage. The roughness can be removed with a hand stone. Two-stroke engines may also suffer from air starvation owing to carbon building up in the transfer and exhaust ports. When transfer ports are partly clogged in this way the result is a loss of power and an increase in fuel consumption. If exhaust ports are partly clogged the result will be overheating and sluggish engine operation.

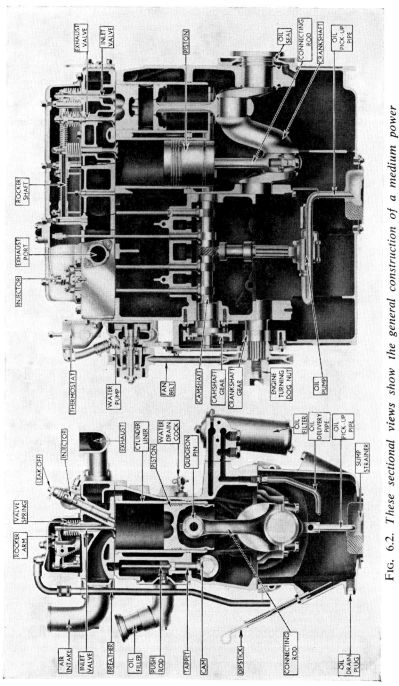

FIG. 6.2. *These sectional views show the general construction of a medium power marine diesel engine, the Perkins Four/270. Using direct fuel injection, this four-cylinder unit develops 58 b.h.p. at 2,000 r.p.m. (compare with Consul petrol engine).*

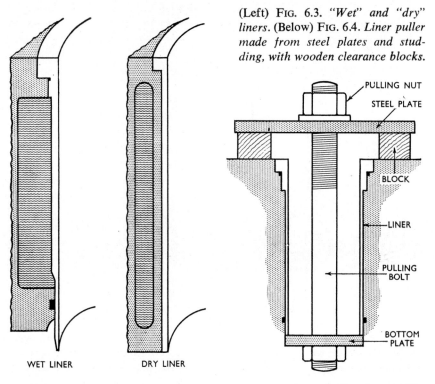

(Left) FIG. 6.3. *"Wet" and "dry" liners.* (Below) FIG. 6.4. *Liner puller made from steel plates and studding, with wooden clearance blocks.*

PULLING NUT

STEEL PLATE

BLOCK

LINER

PULLING BOLT

BOTTOM PLATE

WET LINER   DRY LINER

The cause of port clogging is excessive oil in the petroil mixture. The oil collects on the port edges and burns to form carbon deposits. The carbon should be cleaned off with a stiff wire brush, every trace being removed before the engine is again started.

Cylinder Wear. This causes loss of power, but other troubles have the same effect. The only way to make certain whether excessive wear in the cylinders is the seat of the trouble is to remove the cylinder head and measure the bores accurately. The clearance between the piston and the cylinder wall can be measured with a feeler gauge, as in Fig. 6.5. Clearance in excess of the maker's recommendations is more often due to wear on the cylinder walls than on the piston which is, of course, partly supported by rings.

When wear is obviously considerable and has been rapid, likely causes are :

1. The coolant temperature is too low, interfering with the lubrication of the cylinder walls. Water temperatures must be maintained fairly accurately.

2. The coolant temperature is too high, causing the lubricating oil to

69

FIG. 6.5. *Using a feeler gauge to check piston clearance (shown in broken lines) and measure the gap of a new ring.*

thin out and fail to prevent metal-to-metal contact between rings, piston and cylinder walls.

3. Poor lubrication, due to failure to maintain the lubrication system properly, failure to change the oil at correct intervals, or failure to use the correct grade of oil.

4. Faulty starting methods. When an engine is started it is some time before the oil reaches all moving components, and the cylinders are particularly subject to wear during this period. Correct starting is explained in Chapter 3.

Occasionally trouble is experienced in removing a liner from a diesel engine cylinder block. It can best be extracted by using a puller (Fig. 6.4), first liberally dousing the flange at the top of the liner with rust remover or paraffin oil. If oiled and then left overnight the liner will sometimes come away easily. Alternatively, if the oil sump has been removed the liners can often be freed by giving them a sharp knock from the underside with a soft hammer.

Much of the above maintenance work applies equally to air-cooled engines, and a method of lifting the finned cylinder barrels from their crankcase housings is shown in Fig. 6.6.

FIG. 6.6. *Removing finned cylinder barrel of the air-cooled twin-cylinder Enfield 85 diesel engine. Tapped holes in the barrel take the extractor screws, and a wood block is fitted between the bridge piece and the piston when half way up its stroke. Turning over the engine slowly to raise the piston transmits the movement through the block to the bridge piece and forces out the barrel.*

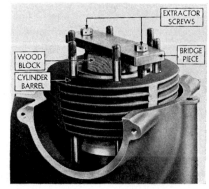

The cylinder head (Fig. 6.7) contains the inlet and exhaust valves in all four-stroke diesels and overhead-valve petrol engines, sometimes the exhaust valve only in uniflow engines, the spray nozzle or injector in many diesels, and the spark plugs in petrol engines. The valve rocker-arm assembly is often bolted to the top of the head, and there are passages for the cooling water inside. Leakage of coolant and of combustion gas between the engine block and the cylinder head is prevented by the use of a gasket or sealing washer.

When a cylinder head fractures—usually between the valve apertures—it must be replaced. Sometimes effective repairs can be made, but with smaller engines it is often cheaper to renew the head. Causes of cylinder head breakage include:

1. Adding cold water to an overheated engine. An engine should never be cooled by pouring cold water into it. If it is necessary to add water in a closed system, the engine should first be allowed to cool. In an emergency cold water can be added in small doses *while the engine is running,* so that the cold water mixes with the hot.

2. Blockage in water passage. If a passage in the cooling system becomes obstructed there is likely to be insufficient heat transfer, with consequent overheating. Cooling passages must be kept clean (see Chapter 11).

3. The cylinder head nuts have not been tightened on their studs in the order prescribed by the engine maker. In this event some studs will take more than their share of the load, there will be deflection of the cylinder head in the area where the nuts are not pulled up tight enough, and breakage can follow. Sometimes when the nuts are not tightened evenly and in the correct sequence, the gasket is pinched in the area around the tight studs and combustion gases blow through where the nuts are not pulled up sufficiently. This causes gasket damage and, worse still, the cylinder head and engine block surfaces may be burned.

4. Cylinder heads can also be damaged by small pieces of metal breaking away from the valves, piston rings or diesel spray nozzles, which obstruct the piston from moving through top centre.

A hissing sound in the vicinity of the cylinder head is probably due to failure of the gasket, which should be renewed immediately.

Sometimes a cylinder head becomes distorted, in which case trouble may be experienced in removing and replacing it. Nothing can be done except to enlarge the stud holes slightly, use a thicker gasket, and put thicker washers between the nuts and the studs. This remedy, by reducing the compression ratio, will lower the engine's efficiency, however.

Sometimes the studs holding the cylinder head break or the threads strip. Damaged studs should at once be renewed. An indication that a stud

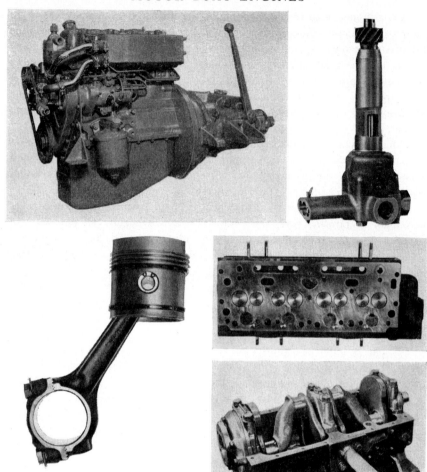

FIG. 6.7. *Perkins Four/99 diesel engine, with component parts which may require attention during overhaul. Shown are a piston assembly, oil pump with driving gear, cylinder head and crankshaft.*

may have broken while the engine is running is given by leakage of water in the vicinity of that stud.

Remember that the cylinder head nuts (or bolts on some engines) should be tightened not only when an engine is being assembled after an overhaul, but after it has been running and attained normal operating temperature.

Cylinder Head Gaskets. Correct fitting of the gasket under the head is important, because on this depends the gas-tight sealing between cylinders and cylinder head which allows proper compression and combustion to take place. Gaskets are made of copper or other soft metal, fibre, rubber or a combination such as copper-clad asbestos. Most petrol engines have one cylinder head gasket, but some diesels use several.

Leakage of the gasket may be shown by the compression of a cylinder being low, which results in difficult starting, or by the escape of water, combustion gases or oil from the joint between the cylinder head and the engine block. This is a good reason for wiping down the engine occasionally; in addition to making the engine look shipshape it enables one to detect leaks from the cylinder head or other joints. When a leak is noticed it should at once be investigated, or worse damage may ensue.

Sometimes there is no external evidence of a leaky gasket, but when the cylinder head is removed the gasket is found to be burned. Depending on the time this condition has been allowed to exist, the cylinder head and the engine block may also be burned, cracked or otherwise damaged in the area of the gasket failure.

A gasket may begin to leak because after prolonged use it has become permanently compressed and lost its ability to conform to irregularities in the metal surfaces. In such a case an attempt is often made to cure the leak by tightening the cylinder head nuts. However, if the gasket is in very poor condition the leak may not be stopped even though the nuts are pulled up to breaking point, and renewal of the gasket is the only real remedy. A gasket should never be used if it is torn or burned, but too often gaskets in such a condition are put back.

Gaskets should, preferably, be renewed every time they are removed. If they are to be used again they should be given a good coating of shellac before being replaced. Rubber and fibre gaskets should, in any case, be renewed after removal.

When a cylinder head is being fitted after an engine inspection or overhaul, the gasket must first be carefully aligned over the studs or bolt holes on top of the engine block. Gaskets are easily damaged by careless treatment and must be treated gently. When the cylinder head has been placed in position over the gasket, all the nuts should be put on their studs and screwed down to finger-tightness. Then they must be tightened evenly and in correct sequence, as shown in the manufacturer's handbook. The amount of turn per nut at each application of the spanner should be such that at least two or three rounds of the cylinder head must be made before final tightening is achieved. The use of a torque wrench is strongly recommended.

PISTONS

Pistons used in marine craft are of conventional design and similiar in all ways to those used in motor cars and motor cycles (Fig. 6.7). The top of the piston is called the crown and the bottom the skirt. The piston itself does not make contact with the cylinder wall, but has a series of rings, fitted into grooves in the piston and projecting a little outwards, which do this. The upper rings (usually two in small engines) are called compression rings, and provide the sealing between piston and cylinder. Most pistons have another ring below these, called an oil-control or scraper ring. This prevents surplus oil from reaching the upper part of the cylinder, where it would eventually foul the combustion space. Sometimes the top ring is termed the firing ring as it is nearest the point where the fuel burns in the cylinder. The piston is carried on its connecting rod by a gudgeon pin which fits into bosses inside the skirt.

Pistons give little trouble provided they receive adequate lubrication and the air that is drawn into the cylinder is free from dust and grit. Removing or "pulling" them is generally not necessary unless a major overhaul is made. When pulled they must be carefully examined and measured to see what has been happening inside the cylinders.

The first indication of piston wear is usually a distinctive slapping or tapping sound called piston slap. This occurs each time the worn piston moves from one side of the cylinder to the opposite side at the top and bottom of its stroke. The sound may disappear as the engine warms up to normal running temperature; this is because the piston has expanded sufficiently to take up the wear. When the slap is pronounced it indicates heavy wear, and it will also be accompanied by a considerable increase in oil consumption and by dirty exhaust smoke. The greater the wear, the dirtier will be the exhaust—but remember that black smoke can be caused by other factors than piston wear.

Piston slap leads to wear of the cylinder walls—it can also be caused by installing a new piston in a badly worn cylinder—with the result that the cylinder walls begin to taper, becoming wider at the top. The rings must then flex to a greater degree than they are normally designed to spring, and oil creeps up into the combustion space where it burns, thus producing black exhaust smoke.

The initial causes of piston wear include poor lubrication due to partial clogging of the oilways in the engine, insufficient oil in the crankcase, the use of dirty, unfiltered oil, and operating the engine at either too high or too low a temperature.

Apart from these, one of the most common causes of wear is starting the engine and then accelerating as soon as it fires. When a cold engine is started the cylinder walls are more or less dry and several crankshaft revolutions must be made before the oil reaches the top of the cylinder. During these few moments, the piston and its rings are sliding on a dry surface and considerable wear results—far more than during hours of normal running with full lubrication. This difficulty cannot be avoided completely, but an engine should not be accelerated as soon as it fires; it should be allowed to idle for a short time and so give the oil time to circulate properly and reach all parts of the cylinders.

There are a few other causes of rapid piston wear. If the air cleaner is dirty or broken or needs servicing, dust and grit can be drawn into the cylinders to mix with the lubricating oil. A very effective grinding paste is thus formed which soon wears down the pistons, rings and cylinder walls. Inadequate cooling of the cylinder block can also lead to wear. The lubricating oil gets overheated, and cannot maintain a film between the moving parts; metal-to-metal contact follows. Also worthy of mention, although rarely encountered, is trouble due to fitting a piston which is slightly too large for the cylinder. Its top will drag against the walls, causing exceedingly heavy wear.

After a piston has been pulled and cleaned by soaking in paraffin oil, diesel fuel or a commercial cleaner, it must be measured across the top both in line with the gudgeon pin and at right-angles to it. Similar pairs of measurements are made at three other points: just above the gudgeon pin, below the gudgeon pin, and at the bottom of the piston. If the wear is in excess of the manufacturer's recommended figures a new piston should be fitted to avoid further trouble and progressive loss of power.

Next, the set of measurements made at right-angles to the crankshaft should be subtracted from those made in line with it, to check on whether the piston has worn oval. A small degree of out-of-roundness is allowable but excessive ovality can cause heavy ring wear. The manufacturer's figures should be consulted and if necessary the piston changed.

Cleaned pistons must be checked for cracks in the crown or top, i.e. the surface which receives the full force of the burning and expanding gases. Look for small surface cracks. If not more than $\frac{1}{4}$ in. in length they can be ignored, but cracks which are obviously creeping towards the edge of the crown from the centre, or tend to form a circle in the centre, are a warning of impending failure. Pistons with such cracks should be changed without delay.

The lands—the portions of the piston wall between the ring grooves— should be checked. If these are badly chipped and small pieces have broken away, a new piston should be fitted to avoid serious trouble later. Land damage can often be traced to badly worn pistons, as in this case the lands hit against the cylinder walls and fracture. Worn cylinders can cause the same trouble.

In some engines, in order to take out the piston, the gudgeon pin must be removed and the connecting rod disconnected. The pin may be retained by circlips or by a pinch bolt in the small end of the connecting rod. If the gudgeon pin is designed to make an interference fit (a very tight fit), it

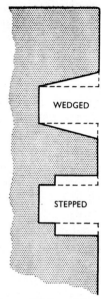

WEDGED

STEPPED

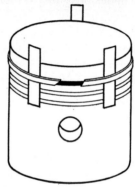

Figs. 6.8 and 6.9. *Piston rings are best removed with a ring expander as above, or the rings can be slipped off over metal strips introduced beneath them at three or more positions as shown in the drawing.*

Fig. 6.10. *Ring grooves may wear to the shapes shown in exaggerated form in this diagram.*

will not be possible to move it when the piston is cold. In this case the piston and connecting rod can be immersed in boiling water for ten minutes and then the pin will usually drop out without much effort. Gudgeon pins should be measured for wear with a micrometer. Wear is usually slight, but inefficient lubrication can result in heavy wear, in which case a new pin should be fitted.

Connecting rods are not subject to conditions which can cause damage in operation, but if the engine should seize up they are liable to bend. Care must be taken in handling them as they are easily damaged if dropped. It is possible to straighten a bent connecting rod in a heavy vice, the jaws of which are fitted with soft metal capping to protect the rod.

Piston Rings. Piston rings are liable to snap easily, and should be extracted from their grooves with care. The best method is to use a ring expander (Fig. 6.8). Alternatively, the rings can be slipped off after short lengths cut from a tin have been introduced beneath them (Fig. 6.9).

After removal each ring should be compared with a new one, and a replacement fitted if the amount of wear is excessive. It is best to measure the wear with a micrometer and compare the reading with the maker's specifications. The amount of permissible wear is never large, otherwise the rings would not seal the piston to the cylinder walls and the combustion gases would blow past into the crankcase. Apart from loss of normal compression, this could result in a crankcase explosion.

When rings are removed, the ring grooves must be cleaned of all carbon, and a good tool for this job is a piece of broken ring used as a scraper. When the groove is perfectly clean the new ring should be inserted and the clearance between the ring and the piston land measured with a feeler gauge. If this is excessive a new piston may be required. This checking is important when new rings are to be fitted, because if the clearance is too small the ring will stick when in use and be unable to seal the piston properly to the cylinder walls. Furthermore, badly fitted oil-control rings can lead to a heavy oil bill, as they will not prevent the oil from pumping into the combustion spaces.

If the clearance is too great it will result in the rings wearing down the lands in the manner shown, somewhat exaggerated, in Fig. 6.10. The only remedy for such a condition is to machine the piston grooves to a larger size and fit over-size rings. There is a definite limit to the amount of metal that can be cut from the grooves and the recutting is a job for experts. It is simpler to buy a new piston, as a rule.

It never pays to operate an engine with a worn set of rings for too long a period. It may well happen that the rings bounce up and down between the lands each time the piston moves, which hammering results in damage to the lands and also further ring wear, until nothing less than the cost of new pistons will put things right.

There are many factors which affect ring life and one cannot lay down any definite schedule for replacing rings. Although engine manufacturers make recommendations, in some engines rings seem to wear faster than in others though both engines may be engaged in the same service and over the same period. It is best, therefore, to adopt a simple inspection plan for the first year of operation. The pistons can be removed regularly at intervals of eight to ten weeks, if the craft is in daily use, and the wear checked with a micrometer. Comparison of these measurements with the maker's wear recommendations will enable one to fix a time limit with reasonable accuracy when rings must be changed in all cylinders.

When new rings are to be fitted the ring gap must be measured (Fig. 6.5). The best way of doing this is to place the ring in the cylinder bore and push it down to about the midway mark, where the cylinder is narrowest, with an inverted piston. The ring will then lie perfectly level and, with the piston withdrawn, the gap can be measured with a feeler gauge.

The gap measurement is then compared with the maker's recommendations. If too small, one end of the ring must be filed until the correct clearance is obtained. This is skilled work, as the clearance must be exact and the two ends must still make a mating joint. The same check must be made on the other rings, remembering that the gap varies for rings in different positions. The scraper or oil-control ring usually has a much smaller gap than the compression rings, as it does not have to withstand such high temperatures. The smaller gap helps to ensure more accurate oil control.

VALVES

Diesel and petrol engines of the four-stroke type as well as uniflow engines use the same kind of valves to admit the incoming air or fuel mixture to the cylinder and provide an exit for the exhaust gases. These valves, of the poppet or mushroom type, are normally extremely efficient and capable of operating for long periods without attention, but are sometimes subject to trouble.

One such trouble is stickiness, when the valve tends to stay open instead of closing properly. A symptom of this in a petrol engine is back-firing. If an exhaust valve is at fault the back-firing will be in the manifold; if it is an inlet valve the back-firing takes place in the carburettor. A diesel with sticky valves will refuse to fire and there may be distinct puffs of black smoke from the exhaust pipe.

The trouble is nearly always due to oil getting baked on the valve stem or its guide. The only remedy when the engine is running is to squirt a mixture of lubricating oil and paraffin oil on the valve stem. This is quite easy with an overhead-valve engine but more difficult with the side-valve type. With a side-valve engine the oil must be squirted upwards into the guides from a forced-feed oilcan.

Trouble with sticking valves may be experienced when an engine is used after it has been laid-up for a long period, because the stems have rusted. For this reason the valves should be given a coating of engine oil when laying-up is undertaken. Other reasons for valves sticking are:

1. Operating the engine with the cooling water too hot or too cold. If the engine temperature is too high the valve stems may warp slightly and stick in their guides. If it is too cold the lubricating oil will oxidise to some extent, forming a thick sludge. When this sludge reaches the valve stems it adheres to them and bakes hard, preventing the free movement of the stems in their guides.

2. Incorrect valve clearances.

3. Valve springs that have become weakened through long use. The only remedy for weak or distorted springs is replacement by new ones. The rest of the valve assembly should be cleaned at the same time.

Springs also break as a result of metal fatigue. The actual breakage of a spring is not always the most serious consequence, however. When a spring breaks it can sometimes allow the valve to drop into the combustion space, in which case the rising piston may strike the valve head and snap it off. The broken head falls into the cylinder and on the next revolution the rising piston can force it through the underside of the cylinder head. Not only will the cylinder head be damaged beyond repair but the connecting rod will be bent, the piston possibly fractured, and all the bearings strained.

If ever a spring fails it must therefore be changed as soon as possible. This is an easy matter and takes only minutes. If the engine is of the overhead-valve type, bring the piston of that cylinder to top dead centre. This will prevent the valve dropping into the cylinder. (If it does fall into the cylinder, the head will have to be lifted to recover it.) The old spring is removed by compressing it with a valve compressor tool and releasing the collet which secures it. After slipping off the spring the valve should be cleaned, and the new spring fitted. Some engines use springs in which the coils are close together at one end. This end must be fitted nearest to the cylinder head to prevent valve bounce.

Valve spring breakage can be minimised by reasonable care in handling, especially when assembling, to avoid scratching the protective enamelling. This may seem a very minor thing but once the enamel is scratched corrosion will follow. The springs should be cleaned in paraffin oil, dried, and checked

FIG. 6.11. *Overhead valve gear of the Enfield 100 single-cylinder diesel engine. Cylinder head nuts are lettered A-F.*

1. *Valve spring*
2. *Spring collar*
3. *Rocker shaft*
4. *Rocker support*
5. *Crankcase*
6. *Securing nut*
7. *Push rod*
8. *Tappet*
9. *Tappet bush screws*
10. *Tappet bush*
11. *Valve rockers*
12. *Lock nut*
13. *Tappet adjuster*
14. *Distance piece*

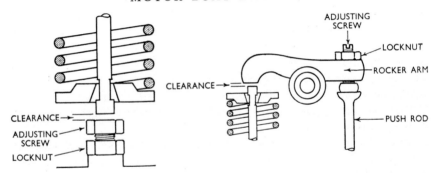

FIGS. 6.12 and 6.13. *Tappet adjustment on* (left) *side-valve engine, and* (right) *overhead-valve engine.*

for chipping of the enamel. Where the enamel has been nicked the damage should be repaired by touching-up with paint. Care should be taken to use springs of the correct strength for replacements (the specifications are given in the maker's handbook). If a spring is too powerful it will cause the valve to pound on its seat, leading to very heavy wear and poor valve seating. It can also reduce the tappet clearance, resulting in the valves opening a little late and closing too early.

Tappet Clearance Adjustment. The valves expand slightly when the engine reaches its normal running temperature, and to allow for this a small clearance must be allowed between the tip of each valve stem and the tappet (on side-valve engines) or rocker arm (on overhead-valve engines). The clearances must be set with considerable accuracy, otherwise there will be noisy running and rapid valve wear. The adjustment is quite simple, however, and is carried out as follows on side-valve engines.

Turn the piston concerned to

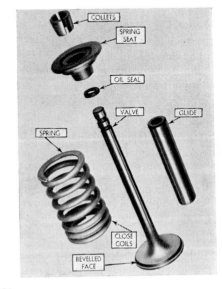

FIG. 6.14. *Typical valve assembly (Ford). The valve spring seat is retained by the collets fitted in the upper groove on the valve stem. The oil seal fits in the lower groove.*

80

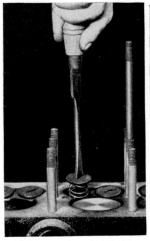
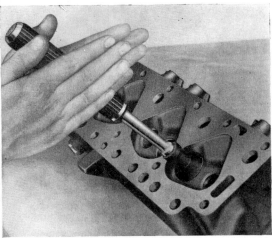

Figs. 6.15 and 6.16. *Grinding-in valves.* Left: *using a screwdriver when the valve head is slotted.* Right: *using a suction cup tool. Note the light spring placed under the valve head when the screwdriver is used.*

top dead centre on its compression stroke. Both valves will now be closed. Measure the clearance between the tappet and the bottom of the valve stem with a feeler gauge. Adjust the tappet by turning in either direction until the correct clearance is obtained—that is, the feeler gauge blade can just be pushed in and out without binding (Fig. 6.12). Lock the tappet in this position with the lock nut, and finally recheck the clearance.

Tappet adjustment is done either while the engine is warm or when cold, depending on the make of engine. The correct clearance figures are often stamped alongside the serial number on the maker's nameplate, or cast on the engine block. If it is stated that the tappets must be set while the engine is warm, then the engine should first be run at idling speed for a few minutes.

A similar method is used to adjust the clearance in overhead-valve engines, except that the adjustment is made by altering a screw adjuster in the end of the rocker arm (Figs. 6.11 and 6.13), the screw being secured in position with a lock nut.

Valves are sometimes burned because of small particles of dirt entering through a defective air cleaner and sticking on the valve or valve seating. The particles prevent the valve from closing fully and hot combustion gases blow through, thus burning the contact faces.

Burned valves must be refaced or ground-in, otherwise their condition will get worse. The job can be done by hand or with power tools.

The hand method can be used when the damage is not severe. The valve

81

spring and collet (Fig. 6.14) are first removed and the valve is then replaced in its guide. With an overhead-valve engine the cylinder head must be taken off and turned over for the operation. The valve is lifted off its seat and a smear of valve-grinding paste placed on both contact surfaces. The valve is then rotated left and right by means of a screwdriver fitting into a slot on the valve head (Fig. 6.15). Alternatively, a brace with a screwdriver bit in the chuck can be used. If the valve heads are not slotted for grinding, a suction cup holding tool, as shown in Fig. 6.16, will have to be used. Continuous rotary motion around the seating must be avoided as a groove will then be cut in the valve and its seat.

This grinding process is continued, lifting the valve from time to time to redistribute the grinding paste, until there is a bright silver-like band of uniform width on the valve and its seat. There must be no trace of rings, "tramlines" or pitting with holes in the contact surfaces.

The grinding paste is wiped off the seat and the valve, and pencil marks are made at half a dozen points spaced equidistantly on the seat. The valve is re-inserted and given one quick half-turn. If all the pencil lines are seen to be cut or rubbed off, the job can be considered satisfactory. If not, grinding (preferably with a fine grade of paste) must be continued until the valve and seat pass this test.

Mechanical equipment makes a better job and is quicker than hand grinding, but the hand method is useful when a top overhaul is carried out and the valves need only a little attention.

If the valve faces are badly worn, refacing will be necessary before grinding in. For this operation, hand tools are available which cut the faces to an exact angle. They are simple to use and fast working, but since different angles are favoured by different manufacturers, it is essential to use a tool of the correct angle.

Replacing Valve Guides and Valve Seats. The guides for the valves in the cylinder block or head should be checked for wear by placing a new valve in the guide and comparing its degree of looseness with that in a new guide. Alternatively, the clearance can be measured. If there is any appreciable play in the guide it should be replaced, otherwise the valve will not seat properly. Guides make a press fit and can be driven out with suitable drifts, or pulled out.

Some engines do not have detachable valve guides, but use plain bores. When wear appears in these bores they must be reamed out and fitted with replacement valves with oversize stems.

Most engines nowadays have detachable valve seats which can be replaced if they become badly burned. The seat, or insert, can be removed with a drift or a puller, difficult seats being pulled more easily if the cylinder head is placed in hot water for about thirty minutes. Inserting the new seat calls for care, and the counterbore in which it fits must be perfectly clean. Some seats can be shrunk into place after the head has been heated.

Damage to valve and seats will be greatly reduced if the air is thoroughly cleaned before it enters the cylinders, and this is another reason why regular servicing of the air cleaner is an important item of maintenance.

CRANKSHAFTS AND BEARINGS

The crankshaft (Fig. 6.17) converts the reciprocating motion of the connecting rods into a steady circular motion which is transmitted to the drive shaft. Crankshafts are generally made from drop-forged steel, heat-treated for additional strength, and with their bearing surfaces hardened for longer wear. Modern crankshafts are balanced to ensure smooth running. A thrust washer or washers is often built into the rear bearing to take up the thrust

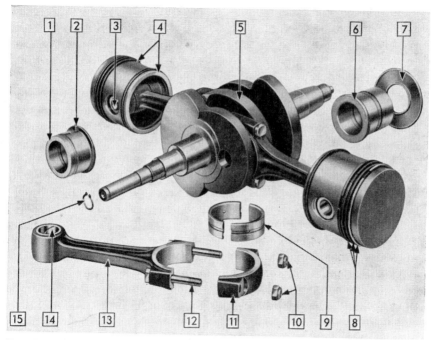

FIG. 6.17. Crankshaft and piston assembly of the Enfield 85 horizontally opposed twin-cylinder diesel engine.

1. Main bearing bush	6. Main bearing bush	11. Connecting rod cap
2. Locating peg	7. Oil flinger	12. Securing bolts
3. Gudgeon pin	8. Compression rings	13. Connecting rod
4. Scraper rings	9. Big end bearing	14. Little end bush
5. Crankshaft	10. Securing nuts	15. Circlip

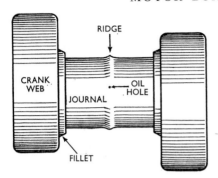

RIDGE

CRANK
WEB

JOURNAL

OIL
HOLE

FILLET

(Left) FIG. 6.18. *Poor lubrication may cause a crankshaft journal to wear unevenly, leaving a ridge in line with the oil hole. Any such ridge must be rubbed down with oiled emery cloth.*

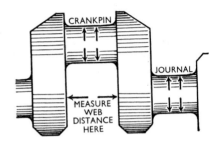

CRANKPIN

JOURNAL

MEASURE
WEB
DISTANCE
HERE

(Right) FIG. 6.19. *Crankpin and journal diameters should be checked for roundness, and the distance between webs measured.*

or push of the propeller shaft or gearing. There is also usually an oil seal to prevent leakage where the crankshaft leaves the engine block, and this seal must be replaced at each overhaul.

In most modern engines the crankshaft bearings (Fig. 6.17) are thin shells fitted into caps or seated in the engine frame; this is often called the precision type of bearing. The shells are semi-circular and can be easily removed and replaced when worn. They give little trouble and have a long life if kept well lubricated. In other engines the bearing metal is bonded to the caps and seats and cannot be removed. The bearing metal has to be scraped to secure a correct fit, which is a long and tiring job.

The bearing shells have a circular groove midway between the bearing ridges. This often runs from parting line to parting line and furnishes registration between the oil holes in the crankshaft. In many cases the lower parts of the bearings are not fitted with oil grooves.

When bearings are taken down for inspection the main bearing caps as well as the connecting rod bearing caps should be removed one at a time. The shells must be checked for scoring, chipping, small cracks, and indications of overheating. Bright spots on the backs of the shells can indicate looseness of the shell in its cap. Overheating will be shown by the presence of black burned oil on the bearing surfaces.

When the crankshaft is to be removed, number each of the bearing caps so that they can be replaced in their former positions. If they are not returned to their original positions trouble can follow as they have to bed themselves in all over again. This can lead to unnecessary wear and sometimes overheating.

With the crankshaft on the bench, the entire length should be cleaned with paraffin oil or other cleaning fluid, and then dried thoroughly to prevent rusting. Next, carefully check each journal for evidence of a ridge at the point in line with the oil hole shown in Fig. 6.18. Any ridge at this point (which naturally receives the best lubrication) must be removed. This can be done by taking a strip of emery cloth soaked in oil and working this backwards and forwards round the ridge.

Then the journals should be measured at the points shown in Fig. 6.19, and these measurements compared with those of the maker. If there has been heavy wear it may be necessary to send the crankshaft ashore to be ground down to the next largest size, while new bearings will also have to be fitted. This, however, is something that is unlikely to be required more than once in the normal lifetime of a marine engine.

The surfaces of the journals must also be inspected for cracks, especially any starting near the oil holes. If present they are a warning that the metal is in poor condition caused by torsional fatigue. Crankshafts damaged in this way are not fit for further service. Also check the fillets for cracks (Fig. 6.18). These again indicate the need for a new crankshaft.

No machining of the main bearings is permissible. The bearing thickness should be measured with outside calipers of a special type, having a steel ball fitted to the anvil. If the amount of wear is greater than that allowed by the engine maker it is better and cheaper to replace them.

When a crankshaft is to be inspected without being removed from the engine, the lower halves of the bearings can be rolled out. The caps are first taken off and then a split pin or suitable bolt is placed in the crankshaft oil hole, the crankshaft is hand-turned and the projecting pin causes the lower bearing shell to roll out of its location. Only one shell should be removed at a time from the lower seats. The others are left to support the crankshaft and avoid the risk of its bowing or bending. Incidentally, if one or two adjoining bearings are worn to a much greater extent than the others this can indicate that the crankshaft is bowed. The shells are replaced by reversing the operation just described, and carefully rolled back into position after first being well lubricated.

In the older type of engines using white metal or babbitt bearing metal bonded to the caps, the bearing clearance is checked by placing lengths of soft lead wire on top of the crankshaft and then tightening the cap. The cap is then removed and the lead wire, flattened by the cap, measured for thickness with a micrometer. It is essential to adhere to the engine maker's recommended clearances for crankshaft bearings.

CAMSHAFTS AND TIMING GEAR

The camshaft is a shaft running parallel with the crankshaft and driven by a train of gears (Fig. 6.20) or by a chain (Fig. 6.21) running over sprockets

1. *Oil pump drive*
2. *Oil pump*
3. *Oil relief valve*
4. *Pressure gauge union*
5. *Oil pipe*
6. *Cam wheel*
7. *Fuel pump cam*
8. *Camshaft gear*
9. *Starting dog*
10. *Camshaft*
11. *Locknut*
12. *Tappet bush*
13. *Fuel pump tappet*
14. *Driving gear*
15. *Weight carrier*
16. *Governor weight*
17. *Sliding sleeve*
18. *Spring collar*
19. *Stop pin*

Fig. 6.20. *Timing gear train on the Enfield 100 single-cylinder diesel engine. Camshaft, oil pump and fuel pump are all crankshaft-driven.*

from one end of the crankshaft. It runs at half the speed of the crankshaft, and its series of cams operate the valves—through the medium of tappets in the case of side-valve engines, or push rods and rocker arms in the case of overhead-valve engines. On many engines the camshaft also carries a skew gear which drives the distributor and the oil pump in the sump. As the cams are integral with the camshaft they cannot be adjusted in any way, and a badly worn camshaft must be replaced.

Camshafts need little attention.

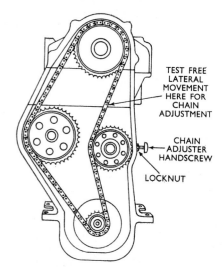

TEST FREE LATERAL MOVEMENT HERE FOR CHAIN ADJUSTMENT

CHAIN ADJUSTER HANDSCREW

LOCKNUT

Fig. 6.21. *Timing chain of the Brit Minor single-cylinder petrol engine. Tension is adjusted by turning the handscrew until the specified degree of play is obtained at the test point.*

Their bearings may need occasional renewing and the cams may be rubbed over lightly with an oilstone if lengthy service has made them slightly uneven, but that is all the attention required.

As the cams on the camshaft must be in a position to open or close the valves according to the position of each piston, the camshaft must be accurately timed to the crankshaft. In order to regain correct timing of the

FIG. 6.22. *Valve timing marks on crankshaft and camshaft sprockets (Ford).*

two shafts in the event of their being removed and refitted, indication marks are usually engraved on the crankshaft drive gear and the camshaft gear (Fig. 6.22). When the lines or dots are in alignment the shafts are correctly timed. If the timing gear consists of a roller chain running over sprockets, the timing marks will be found on the sprockets.

With a geared arrangement an idler gear is often placed between the crankshaft and camshaft gears to transmit the drive; otherwise inconveniently large gear wheels would have to be used to bridge the gap and bring the camshaft down to half engine speed. Such idler gears are also marked for timing.

With a chain-type timing gear, it is important to keep the chain well lubricated, and it always has its own supply of oil from the sump. Chains must also be carefully aligned and tightened to prevent mistiming. If a chain has been running out of alignment it will have bright marks on one inner face of each link, while the other inner face will be dull or oily.

CHAPTER 7

Fuel and Exhaust Systems

In this chapter we shall consider the fuel supply to the engine, and the arrangements for disposing of exhaust gases. In a diesel engine the fuel in use is diesel oil, of course. In a petrol engine the fuel is not, strictly speaking, liquid petrol but a mixture of atomised petrol and air. (Vaporizing-oil engines use a mixture consisting of vaporized kerosene and air.) The supply system for a marine petrol engine, therefore, comprises a petrol tank, a pump to draw petrol from the tank to the engine (except where gravity feed is used), a carburettor which produces a suitable mixture of petrol and air for delivery to the engine, a cleaner for removing dust and grit from air before it enters the carburettor, and the necessary pipes or connecting tubing.

For a diesel installation no carburettor is required, but instead there is a fuel injection pump, as described in Chapter 8. For a vaporizing-oil engine a special type of carburettor is needed, with a supply of vaporizing oil or kerosene, and also petrol for starting purposes.

CARBURETTORS

Of the various components in the petrol fuel system mentioned above, the carburettor (Fig. 7.1) is undoubtedly the least understood by the average operator. Some modern automobile carburettors are extremely complex in design, but those in general use on small marine craft are quite simple and reliable.

The carburettor receives a supply of liquid petrol from the fuel tank and atomises it—that is, forces it through a very small hole or jet so that it is broken up into a fine mist or spray. At the same time the

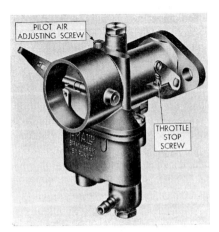

FIG. 7.1. *Amal type 398 carburettor, as fitted to many small engines.*

carburettor receives a supply of clean air from the air intake and mixes this with the atomised petrol to form a suitable fuel mixture. The normal proportions of this mixture are about 15 parts of air to one part of petrol, by weight. However, the requirements of the engine vary in this respect and the carburettor must be designed to vary both the mixture and the quantity supplied to the cylinders in accordance with the engine's speed and load. The fuel mixture enters the intake manifold and then passes through the inlet valves into the cylinders to be compressed and ignited.

It is important to bear in mind that the sole function of the carburettor is to deliver a fuel mixture to the engine—engine troubles are often wrongly attributed to the carburettor, when a little thought may show that the fault must lie elsewhere.

Fig. 7.2 is a cross-sectional drawing of a Zenith V-type carburettor. That shown is a vertical type, but the horizontal and downdraught types are very

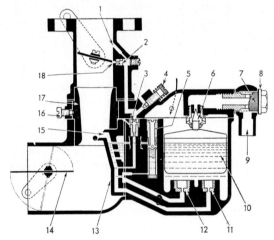

FIG. 7.2 *Zenith vertical carburettor.* (*Numbers refer to explanation in the text.*)

similar in principle. Referring to this illustration, from the supply tank the petrol passes through the feed pipe and enters the carburettor at the union 9. The flow continues through the filter 7 and enters the float chamber through the needle valve 6. Passing through the main jet 11 and compensating jet 12, petrol flows along the passages to a common channel in the emulsion block 13. The flow continues until the channels and float chamber are filled to a predetermined height. The flow is then cut off due to the float 10 having risen and pressed the needle valve against its seating. As fuel is used by the engine, the float will fall and the valve open, allowing more petrol to enter. The amount of petrol in the carburettor is thus automatically regulated by the float and needle valve, to prevent flooding of the unit.

The air supply to the carburettor is via the large opening at the bottom left of the drawing. Just inside is a strangler flap *14* (also known as a choke valve). When an engine is started from cold, a rich fuel mixture—one containing more than the normal proportion of petrol—is required, and this is obtained by using the choke control which operates the strangler flap. Pulling the control knob outward from the instrument panel causes the flap to turn, as indicated in the drawing, and cut off the flow of air into the carburettor. The suction created in the inlet manifold by the pistons on their induction stroke is then directed entirely on the petrol jets, and consequently a very "rich" mixture is supplied. Opening the strangler flap progressively increases the intake of air from the atmosphere and so reduces the richness of the fuel mixture, until there is maximum inflow of air when the flap is horizontal, as shown.

In cases of difficult starting it is often helpful to pull out the choke control fully (i.e. close the strangler flap), and turn over the engine once or twice with the ignition switched off. Then switch on the ignition and start the engine in the normal way.

There is another flap valve in the outlet through which the fuel mixture is delivered to the engine (top of drawing). This valve is called the throttle, and by turning it so as to restrict the outlet the quantity of fuel mixture passing can be controlled. This in turn controls the speed of the engine. The throttle lever which moves the flap is shown on the illustration; on most marine craft it is connected to a hand throttle control.

The strangler is usually interconnected with the throttle by exterior linkage, so that the throttle automatically opens the right amount when the choke control is operated. With carburettors of different design it is recommended that for starting purposes the throttle be slightly opened by means of the hand control; the correct setting will soon be found by experiment. Where a fully automatic strangler is fitted the flap is free to move on an offset spindle and is held closed by means of a light coil spring while the engine is idle or being started from cold. As additional suction is created after the engine has started the tension of the spring is overcome and the flap opens to admit air.

With the strangler open (i.e. choke control fully home) and the throttle in the idling position, the carburettor will be working as follows. The engine depression or suction will be concentrated on the outlet *1*, which in turn will be directed on the slow-running jet *3*. Consequently petrol will be drawn from the well beneath the jet, measured as it passes through, and meet the air entering at the base of the adjusting screw *4*. The amount of petrol issuing from the slow-running jet is controlled by this screw.

At the throttle edge there is a further outlet *18*, which breaks into the slow-running channel. As the throttle is opened from the idling position this provides additional fuel mixture to ensure a progressive speed-up of the engine. The jet used is called the progressive jet (2).

When the throttle is opened still further the suction will be concentrated at the "beak" 15 of the emulsion block which projects into the narrowest part of the choke tube 17. This will first result in petrol being drawn from the main channel in the emulsion block, situated beneath the slow-running jet 3, and from the well under the capacity tube 5, so that when the engine is running at normal speed the supply of petrol comes through the main and compensating jets (11 and 12).

Carburettors supplied as original equipment always have jet settings that have been carefully calculated as being the most suitable for the engine concerned, and very few adjustments to the unit are normally required. When a replacement carburettor is fitted, care should be taken to ensure that it has the same jet settings. In general, a carburettor will give the best service if adjustments are made only when absolutely necessary.

Carburettor Maintenance. Adjustment to the slow-running controls is all that is likely to be needed normally, apart from occasional cleaning of the main and compensating jets, float chamber and filter. To get at the float chamber and jets it is necessary to take out the two bolts which support the bowl of the carburettor. One hand should be placed beneath the bowl during this operation so that it will not drop into the bilges. Remove the bowl complete and pour the petrol in it back into the tank.

The float and needle valve can be lifted out and put on one side where there is no chance of them being damaged or getting dirty. Any trace of dirt or grit on the needle valve must be carefully cleaned off, otherwise carburettor

FIG. 7.3. *Unscrewing the main and compensating jets of a Zenith carburettor, using one of the square-ended float-chamber bolts as a key. The float is shown on the left.*

flooding will occur later. The two brass jets will be visible screwed into the bottom of the float chamber. On older units the jets have slots in them and are unscrewed with a screwdriver. Recent models have jets with a square recess instead of a slot. One of the two fixing bolts has a squared end and can be used as a key to unscrew the jets (Fig. 7.3).

When cleaning the jets do not prod them with wire or sharp implements,

(Right) FIG. 7.4A. *Zenith 30VIG-6 carburettor with float chamber removed to reveal the jets, needle valve and accelerator pump. Note the squared recesses in the jets to permit removal by the key-type holding bolts.*

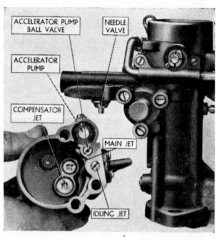

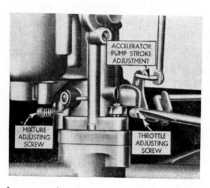

(Left) FIG. 7.4B. *Adjustable controls for slow running on the same Zenith carburettor. The pump stroke adjustment is not normally needed for marine use.*

because the slightest damage will affect the accurately calibrated orifices. The most satisfactory and efficient method is to wash the jet in petrol and blow through it in the reverse direction to the normal flow.

The slow-running jet *3* is provided with a screwdriver slot for removal. This also applies to the screw holding the capacity tube. When this screw is removed and inverted the capacity tube will fall out. (Not all carburettors have a separate capacity tube, however. In some the tube is actually cored to the required size during manufacture.) The emulsion block is held to the side of the bowl by screws. Both the starting jet *3* and the progressive jet *2* are also removable with a screwdriver, but with the latter the plugging screw in the outer casing must be removed first.

Correct slow-running is obtained by adjusting the throttle stop screw and air regulating screw (Fig. 7.4). The stop screw determines the idling speed of the engine because it affects the throttle position. To increase the idling speed the stop screw is turned inwards; to decrease the idling speed it is unscrewed. The air regulating screw varies the proportions of petrol and air (i.e. the "richness") of the mixture delivered to the engine when it is idling with the throttle closed. With this type of carburettor the best position for the air regulating screw is about $\frac{1}{2}$ to $1\frac{1}{2}$ turns from the fully-home position. Some models have a long taper on the control screw, and in these cases the normal adjustment is within three turns.

If the engine will not idle for any length of time, or stalls when reduced to idling speed, the slow-running jet (*3*, Fig. 7.2) may be choked and need cleaning. After examination the throttle and air adjusting screws will need resetting. If the engine "hunts" or runs with uneven surges at idling speed this indicates that the fuel mixture is too rich and must be weakened by turning the air regulating screw in an anti-clockwise direction.

The carburettor is by no means the only cause of poor idling, however, and when this trouble occurs other factors should be considered before condemning the carburettor out of hand. Air leaks at unions or joints, worn valve guides, badly seating valves, poor tappet adjustment, ignition too far advanced, and incorrect gaps at the spark-plug points are all possible causes.

Most other carburettors work on a similar principle to the one described here, but there are often slight differences in the method used to control the fuel mixture. The adjustment procedure is always clearly explained in the maker's handbook.

VAPORIZING-OIL CARBURETTORS

Vaporizing oil or petrol/paraffin engines use carburettors of a somewhat different design from those just described. Fig. 7.5 shows a Solex carburettor which is designed to operate normally on vaporizing oil but to use petrol for starting and warming-up the engine. The petrol starting device is actually an auxiliary carburettor built into the main unit and can be seen on the right of the illustration.

The lever 9 is connected to the control panel and operated by a cable. When the control is pulled outwards the lever rotates the open position and the valve plate 14 also rotates, so that a hole in the plate registers with the opening 6 in the carburettor throttle tube. Meanwhile petrol has entered at 11 and passed through the calibrated jet 12 to form a reserve to give the initial rich starting mixture. This reserve is controlled by a needle valve 13.

When the engine is turned over with the throttle closed, suction occurs at 6 and is transmitted to the secondary plate 7 which is drawn inwards against the resistance of an expansion spring having a predetermined resistance value. Simultaneously, the suction takes effect on the underside of the needle head-plate 10, withdrawing the needle from its seating and allowing the petrol to pass through to the mixing chamber where it is emulsified and "corrected" by the air entering at 8. The engine fires this rich mixture.

After a few seconds the lever 9 must be moved to the intermediate position, determined by a marked resistance to the movement as the spring-loaded ball registers with the deep pit in the lever. In this position the valve plate 14 at the opposite end of the shaft has rotated so that a smaller hole in the plate registers at the point 6. The result is that the mixture passing to the cylinders is reduced in richness to avoid "overdosing."

The engine is now rapidly warming up and it can soon be determined when it is hot enough to switch over to the heavier vaporizing-oil fuel. To make the change the lever *9* must be moved to the opposite stop by pushing the dashboard control fully home. The valve plate *14* then presents a blank surface to the opening and the petrol supply is cut off. The engine depression or suction now acts on the main jet *17* which draws vaporizing oil from the float chamber, the flow being controlled by needle valve *1*. The pilot jet *3* is supplied with air through the bleed passage *2*.

When the engine is idling with the throttle *5* almost closed, suction occurs at the hole of which the effective area is regulated by the volume control screw *4*. The fuel is drawn up the vertical channel via the hole below the lower edge of the throttle and additionally by the air entering the carburettor air bleed *2*. The quantity of fuel and the idling strength is regulated by adjusting the screw *4*. (Unscrewing this control enriches the mixture; screwing it in weakens the mixture.)

The main jet delivers the emulsified air in the following manner. The jet *17* is seated in a carrier and held by the jet cap *16* screwed to the carrier. Air entering the holes *18* rises to the top and descends into the annulus between the main jet via the holes in the side. The result is that a mixture of air and fuel issuing from the top of the spraying assembly is finally emulsified by the main air stream passing through the choke tube *15* on its way to the engine.

Should the engine fail to run under load when the carburettor is changed

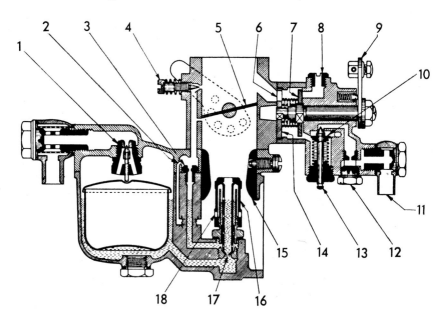

FIG. 7.5. *Solex FV3 carburettor for vaporizing oil, with petrol starting device. (Numbers refer to the explanation in the text.)*

FIG. 7.6. *Construction of one type of vaporizer unit for vaporizing-oil engines. The hot exhaust gases are used to heat the fuel mixture on its way to the engine.*

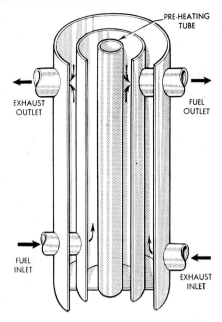

 over from petrol to vaporizing oil, the starter control can again be operated so that petrol is used to assist the heavier fuel as a temporary measure. Engine manifolds for this type of carburettor are designed with special "hot spots" to allow the heavier fuel to be used efficiently when the engine has warmed up.

Some vaporizing-oil engines employ a separate vaporizer unit, in addition. This utilises the heat of the exhaust gases to warm up the fuel mixture before it enters the engine manifold. As shown in Fig. 7.6, the device consists of two tubes, the outer carrying the exhaust gas and the inner the fuel mixture. A blow torch can be inserted in the hollow centre to pre-heat the vaporizer for cold-weather starting.

FUEL SUPPLY TROUBLES

When fuel problems arise operators are often inclined to lay the blame immediately on the carburettor. In fact, trouble in service is much less likely from this component than from elsewhere in the fuel system—somewhere between the tank filler cap and the carburettor petrol pipe union.

Again, if an engine stops without warning and refuses to restart it is a common reaction to turn to the fuel tank immediately on the assumption that the fuel has been exhausted. This may be so, but normally the engine does not stop suddenly when the petrol supply is cut off. It is more likely to slow down, cough and finally splutter to a stop. When it stops suddenly the cause of the trouble is more likely to be found in the ignition circuit than the petrol system.

If trouble is suspected in the petrol system, first take off the filter bowl and check that the filter is clean. Examine the contents of the filter bowl. If there is water present it will be separated. If the bowl is transparent (Fig. 7.7) it is quite possible to distinguish the different layers of petrol and water. A useful way of learning how to identify water in filter bowls is to mix a

FIG. 7.7. *An easily installed Amal petrol filter with transparent nylon bowl for visual checking of the sediment. Nylon material is also used for the gauze filter element.*

little water with petrol in a test tube and watch the water and petrol separate into two layers. If water has been discovered in the filter bowl it is reasonable to suppose that it has also been sucked into the carburettor float chamber. The float chamber should, therefore, be detached by removing the fixing bolts, and its contents drained off.

Water in the petrol can be caused by condensation of water vapour from the air inside the petrol tank. When petrol is drawn from the tank to supply the engine, air enters to take its place through the tank vent. This vent may be merely a hole in the tank filler cap, but more often it is a tube of small diameter rising well above deck level. When an engine has been stopped overnight the air cools and the vapour condenses into water which settles at the tank bottom. When the engine is later started this water may be drawn through the carburettor into the engine, which then stops working. The remedy for this trouble is to fill the tank fully when an overnight stop is made.

When water has settled to the bottom of the tank, as shown by its presence in the filter bowl, the contaminated supply should be drained off. This is an easy matter if the tank is fitted with a drain tap or valve, or if the petrol pipe is connected to the tank bottom. All that is necessary is to open the valve or tap or disconnect the fuel line at a point where it is convenient to place a container to catch the contaminated petrol (about half a pint). But do not remove the pipe completely or the fuel will spurt everywhere before the connecting nut can be replaced. Merely slacken the nut back a couple of turns and allow the water-petrol mixture to run out slowly.

Some engines take their fuel supplies through the top of the tank, as in Fig. 7.8. In such cases the bottom of the tank can be pumped out with a bicycle pump having its tyre connector in place, if necessary. Alternatively, it can be siphoned out by inserting a small-diameter flexible tube in the bottom of the tank through the filler cap and leading the other end to a container located below the level of the tank bottom. A quick suck is taken at the free end to start the petrol flowing down into the container. It will continue until the tube is lifted above the level of the remaining petrol in the tank.

A drawback with this method is that one is almost bound to receive at least a taste, if not a mouthful, of the water-petrol mixture, and this is far from pleasant. There is a way of avoiding this, however. Submerge the tube to be used over the side until it is full of water and there are no bubbles rising from either end. Pinch one end closed and withdraw the tube. Insert the free end in the petrol tank and take the pinched end to the bottom of the container. Release the end of the tube and the mixture should start running from the tank. If the tube will not stay at the bottom of the tank but twists and turns, it can be lightly lashed to a length of wood, thin enough to be inserted with the tube through the filler orifice.

Sometimes petrol pipes become choked, due to failure to clean out the fuel system thoroughly when the engine is overhauled or through using contaminated petrol. (The latter trouble will soon arise if the practice is made of carrying fuel aboard in rusty cans.) If a supply pipe from the bottom of the tank seems to be choked, loosen the connexion at the carburettor and turn

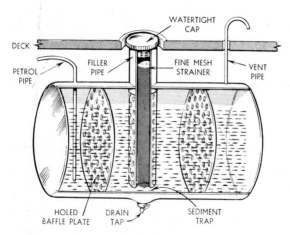

FIG. 7.8. A well designed petrol tank should be fitted with baffles, a deep filling tube with removable strainer, and a sediment trap.

on the tap or valve. Fuel should flow through the loosened union. If it does not, disconnect the pipe at the tank and see if fuel just trickles through when the tap is opened very slightly. Then open the tap or valve quickly and shut it off if the petrol gushes out. This will show whether the obstruction is inside the tank. If it is somewhere in the pipe, disconnect the pipe at both ends and blow through it. Should blowing fail to clear the obstruction, push a length of soft wire through.

If the line remains choked and the engine must be operated, it is often possible to make a connexion between the carburettor and the tank with a length of plastic tubing. Rubber can be used, but is liable to be dissolved by petrol and bits of rubber breaking away may choke the carburettor jets. If no tubing is available it may be possible to take the choked pipe ashore. Choosing a safe place, wet the pipe with petrol and set this alight. The heat may loosen the obstruction sufficiently for it to be dislodged. Only a very small amount of petrol should be used if this method is resorted to, otherwise any soldered joints in the pipe will melt, and burning petrol can be dangerous, of course.

When a suitable length of tubing is available on board, one end must be fixed to the petrol union on the carburettor and the other end to the tap or valve at the bottom of the fuel tank. If there is difficulty in fixing the tubing to the tap it may be necessary to cut off the first six inches of pipe from the tank, including the flared end and connecting nut. The pipe length can then be replaced and the tubing slipped over it, well wrapped with string at both ends to stop it slipping off. This emergency rig will enable the craft to reach home, when the cut-off petrol pipe can be replaced without much trouble.

While this flexible tubing is in use the engine must be run at reduced speed, as there is the risk that the suction of the engine or its pump will be strong enough to make the tubing walls collapse slightly and reduce the flow of petrol to a trickle.

As soon as possible, the dirty tank must be taken ashore for cleaning. It should be well washed out with a garden hose and allowed to drain and dry thoroughly before being replaced.

Cracks and breakages sometimes develop in the petrol piping owing to poor installation. Common faults in this respect are bending the pipe at right angles and providing insufficient support, which leads to fractures due to vibration. When a pipe fractures while the craft is under way the only cure is to shut down the engine and drain the pipe. Wipe it as dry as possible, then bind a surgical plaster or something similar over the break. Insulating tape can be used but this will not stick to a petrol-wetted pipe, so both the first turns and the last few would have to be made around the pipe at a dry point.

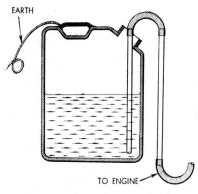

Use stout string to hold the "plaster" in position, with each turn lying tightly against the preceding one. When plastic tubing is available the damaged section of pipe can be cut out and the sawn ends reconnected with plastic tubing. (Neoprene can be recommended for this purpose.)

Fig. 7.9. *Simple emergency fuel system made from a petrol can and tubing arranged as a siphon.*

If the layout of the fuel system has been badly planned, the fuel pipe may run too near a hot exhaust pipe, manifold, or other source of heat, and trouble can then arise due to vapour lock. This means that the petrol vaporizes before it reaches the carburettor, and the engine does not obtain the correct fuel mixture. When this trouble arises, the engine must be stopped for a while and the fuel supply line allowed to cool. Wrap the piping in wet rags before restarting the engine, and keep these damp during the remainder of the journey. For a permanent cure the piping must either be re-routed or cased in with asbestos. Re-routing is much to be preferred, if it can be arranged.

When an obstructed fuel pipe cannot be cleared, repaired or by-passed as described above, it is still possible to keep the engine running for some time by the use of a short length of tubing. Siphon or drain off a few pints of fuel into a suitable can and lash the can to some convenient support. Place one end to start the flow of fuel through the tubing, and then attach the free end to the carburettor union or inlet pipe (see Fig. 7.9).

Fuel Pumps. Many engines are fitted with a pump to supply the carburettor with petrol (Fig. 7.10). When fuel pump trouble is indicated,

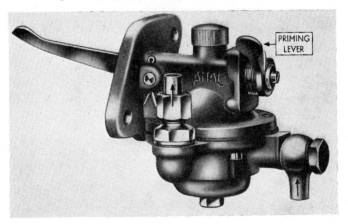

FIG. 7.10. *Amal petrol or diesel fuel pump, capacity 60 pints per hour. The operating principle is similar to that shown in Fig. 7.11.*

disconnect the petrol pipe at the carburettor and place a can beneath the open pipe end. Switch off the engine and press the starter or hand-crank the engine. If the pump is working fuel will be ejected from the pipe in small spurts.

If the pump fails to deliver any fuel it may merely need cleaning. This is done by dismantling and washing the internal suction and delivery valves in petrol (Figs. 7.11 and 7.12). If the pump has failed because of some

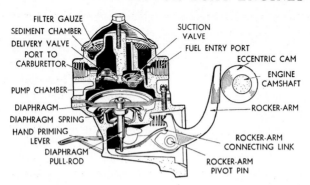

FILTER GAUZE
SEDIMENT CHAMBER
DELIVERY VALVE
PORT TO
CARBURETTOR
PUMP CHAMBER
DIAPHRAGM
DIAPHRAGM SPRING
HAND PRIMING
LEVER
DIAPHRAGM
PULL-ROD

SUCTION
VALVE
FUEL ENTRY PORT
ECCENTRIC CAM
ENGINE
CAMSHAFT
ROCKER-ARM
ROCKER-ARM
CONNECTING LINK
ROCKER-ARM
PIVOT PIN

FIG. 7.11. *Construc-*
tion of an AC fuel
feed pump. Opera-
tion of the dia-
phragm from the
engine camshaft
draws fuel in
through the suction
valve and discharges
it to the carburettor
through the delivery
valve.

mechanical defect such as a damaged diaphragm, and cannot be repaired on the spot, it may still be possible to start the engine by by-passing the pump. All that has to be done is to disconnect the pump at both ends and connect the two ends of the petrol pipe together. If the pump is situated below the level of the fuel tank and is gravity fed, petrol will flow down the pipe to the carburettor in sufficient quantity to run the engine slowly.

The problem is more difficult when the tank is situated below the pump. Efforts must then be made to pressurise the petrol tank in order to get the petrol to flow, using a bicycle pump. First, the filler cap is plugged or a piece of cloth tied over the cap to prevent air escaping past the threads. The tank vent is connected in some fashion to the bicycle pump. This can be done by cutting off the metal end of the flexible tyre connector, forcing the tube into the vent pipe and binding it in place with insulating tape. Air pressure in the tank is then built up by hand pumping, so that fuel is forced along the supply pipe to the carburettor.

But few craft carry a bicycle pump. The alternative then is to siphon out

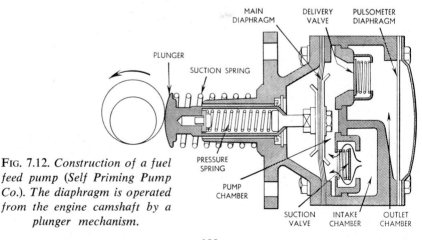

MAIN
DIAPHRAGM
DELIVERY
VALVE
PULSOMETER
DIAPHRAGM
PLUNGER
SUCTION SPRING
PRESSURE
SPRING
PUMP
CHAMBER
SUCTION
VALVE
INTAKE
CHAMBER
OUTLET
CHAMBER

FIG. 7.12. *Construction of a fuel*
feed pump (Self Priming Pump
Co.). The diaphragm is operated
from the engine camshaft by a
plunger mechanism.

100

the fuel into a can and make a temporary hook-up near the carburettor as shown in Fig. 7.9.

Even without a petrol pump some engines will suck fuel from the tank in sufficient quantity to keep running at a reduced speed. If an engine runs for a while without the pump working there is no reason why it should stall unless the fuel is shut off. This can happen if the pump valves close and there is insufficient suction to open them again. When this is suspected the valves can be removed for servicing and replaced, or in an emergency they can be removed so that petrol will continue to flow through the non-operative pump. Alternatively, the pump can be by-passed as already described. If the faulty pump is electrically operated, the supply lead should be disconnected and secured in a safe place.

CARBURETTOR TROUBLES

Carburettors rarely go wrong. Provided the slow-running and mixture controls are properly adjusted in the first place, all that is necessary is to ensure that the fuel supply is kept clean through proper filtering and that all trace of water or moisture is kept out of the system. When an overhaul is made the carburettor should be dismantled and the parts well washed in paraffin. New jets may be required, but only after lengthy service. The throttle valve and choke bearings may also wear.

When a carburettor is known to be getting a sufficient supply of petrol but the engine will not fire—and the fault is believed to lie in the fuel system —a quick carburettor check can be carried out as follows:

1. See that the choke and throttle valves are working properly and their controls are not loose.

2. Check the float. Ensure that it floats properly by jiggling the valve needle.

3. Check the air intake horn after removing the spark arrester or air cleaner. Look carefully for any wet patch on the surfaces. If there is petrol inside the air intake or horn it is a fairly certain sign that the float is sticking and not shutting off the petrol, causing the carburettor to flood. In this case, try to free the float by giving the carburettor body a smart thump with the heel of the hand. This should be sufficient to release the float if it has merely been jammed in the open position by a particle of dirt which has passed through a defective fuel filter.

If the float still does not function after this treatment the reason may be that it is punctured. The float should be taken out and tested by shaking it. The presence of petrol inside indicates that the float is punctured and needs replacing. If a spare float is not immediately available, a repair can be made by draining out the petrol and then sealing the puncture with the slightest possible smear of solder. When no soldering equipment is available a

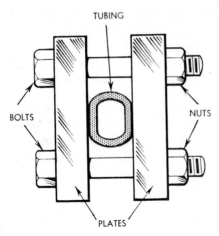

TUBING

BOLTS

NUTS

PLATES

FIG. 7.13. *A simple flow control clamp for use on a temporary flexible fuel line. Accurate control is provided by the screw adjustment.*

temporary repair can be made by plugging the hole with a small wood screw. Even a splinter of wood can be used if the hole is at the top or bottom, or a length of surgical plaster can be tied over it with very thin string. In the latter case the repair must not interfere with the movement of the float and the string must not be pulled so tightly as to collapse the float metal or distort it unduly.

If the float has corroded badly it may simply disintegrate. When this happens, and an emergency repair is necessary to enable the craft to get home, the best thing to do is to turn off the petrol at the tank and carefully wipe up all spilled petrol. Allow damp spots to dry out, then replace the damaged float and turn on the petrol very gradually so that just sufficient seeps past the needle valve and into the float chamber to allow the engine to run, but not to flood the carburettor. The petrol flow can be gradually increased until the engine stalls once more because of flooding. Wipe up the spilled petrol and re-start the engine. This time the flow should be restricted a little more so as to avoid further flooding.

If there is no tap or valve between the tank and the carburettor or if the control is stuck hard and cannot be moved, as may happen in poorly maintained craft, the flow can be controlled by inserting a length of flexible tubing in the line and squeezing it to regulate the amount entering the float chamber. As it is difficult to maintain even pressure all the time with thumb and fingers, a clamp should be improvised from a pair of holed plates (end pieces of a tin can will do) connected by two nuts and bolts as shown in Fig. 7.13. The nuts can be tightened as necessary to give accurate control of the quantity reaching the carburettor. Spring-type paper clips can also be used, with slips of wood between the jaws to prevent the fuel being completely shut off, or the flow can be restricted by binding the flexible tubing with string.

These methods, though rather primitive, will often allow a boat to get home without recourse to oars, poling, or being towed. Carburettor troubles are best avoided, however, by inspecting the parts at regular intervals. A good carburettor costs little more than a cheap one but is well worth the difference. Special marine types made of rust-resisting metals are strongly to be recommended.

Incidentally, if the petrol supply is almost exhausted, paraffin oil can sometimes be used as emergency fuel, if there is any available. The engine should be accelerated to its top speed just before the petrol becomes exhausted. The increased speed will heat up the metal of the intake manifold and the carburettor body. Add paraffin from the cooking stove, emergency lamp or other containers to the tank. The engine may run on the heavy fuel accompanied by a great deal of spluttering and back-firing, but if it gets the craft to a supply point any amount of spluttering is better than drifting.

When the carburettor fails completely the only possible chance of moving the boat is to soak a sponge in petrol and partly stuff it into the carburettor's air horn. The spark arrestor or air cleaner must first be removed, of course. Petrol evaporating from the sponge will mix with incoming air and may be sufficient to run the engine slowly. Early carburettors worked on a somewhat similar principle, using wicks instead of sponges. Rags are often better than sponges for this job as they allow a better air flow.

Fuel Supply Safety Precautions. Whenever the petrol line or tank or anything connected with the fuel service has been taken down for repair or adjustment and fuel has been spilt into the craft, the engine and hull spaces should be well ventilated before any attempt is made to start the engine. Petrol fumes are very explosive and negligence in venting the engine compartment and other spaces before getting under way has caused the loss of more than one vessel.

When working on the fuel system there should be no smoking, no cooking, nor the use of any electrical apparatus. When taking petrol aboard, pouring it from a can to the tank, or using a can as an emergency tank, always earth the can so as to avoid the risk of static electricity being discharged in the form of a spark. Such a spark can be sufficient to ignite fumes from the petrol and cause an explosion. The can is easily earthed by resting it on the metal funnel into the tank. An emergency fuel tank should always be fitted with an earth wire as shown in Fig. 7.9.

AIR FILTRATION

Every engine should be fitted with an air cleaner to extract dust and grit from the air passing into the carburettor and thence to the cylinders. If these impurities are not filtered out the result will be rapid wear on pistons, piston rings and cylinders, damage to other components caused by grit entering the lubricating oil, and wear and obstruction inside the carburettor. On diesel engines the air cleaner is fitted to the end of the air intake manifold; on petrol engines it is attached to the air horn leading the carburettor.

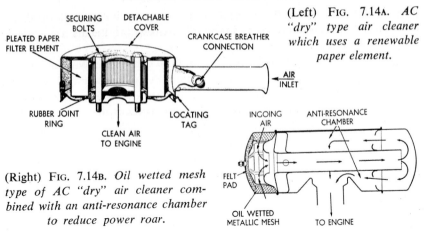

SECURING BOLTS — DETACHABLE COVER — PLEATED PAPER FILTER ELEMENT — CRANKCASE BREATHER CONNECTION — AIR INLET — RUBBER JOINT RING — LOCATING TAG — CLEAN AIR TO ENGINE — INGOING AIR — ANTI-RESONANCE CHAMBER — FELT PAD — OIL WETTED METALLIC MESH — TO ENGINE

(Left) FIG. 7.14A. *AC "dry" type air cleaner which uses a renewable paper element.*

(Right) FIG. 7.14B. *Oil wetted mesh type of AC "dry" air cleaner combined with an anti-resonance chamber to reduce power roar.*

There are two types of cleaner in general marine use, the "dry" or wire wool type and the "wet" or oil-bath type. In the usual dry type, impurities are filtered out as the air is drawn through a fine gauze screen or wire-wool filter (Fig. 7.14B). The filtering medium can be wetted with a medium-weight oil to increase its efficiency, engine oil being commonly used for the purpose. The only maintenance required is to clean the filtering medium at regular intervals. If the filter becomes choked and restricts the inflow of air, the engine will be difficult to start, fuel consumption figures will rise, the engine will overheat, and dirty exhaust smoke will be emitted.

Cleaning is simple. The filtering element is withdrawn and washed by swirling it in a bath of petrol or paraffin oil. The element is drained dry and then refitted. It must not be installed when wet, or the fumes will be sucked in with the fuel and cause excessive high pressures to develop in the cylinders, accompanied by detonation.

Another type of "dry" air cleaner is shown sectioned in Fig. 7.14A. This type uses a paper element which must be renewed about every 10,000 miles.

The wet type of air cleaner is steadily gaining in popularity in all classes of inboard engines. This utilises a bath of engine oil, as shown in Fig. 7.15. The air enters the cleaner and impinges on the surface of the oil with sufficient

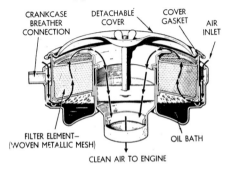

CRANKCASE BREATHER CONNECTION — DETACHABLE COVER — COVER GASKET — AIR INLET — FILTER ELEMENT (WOVEN METALLIC MESH) — OIL BATH — CLEAN AIR TO ENGINE

FIG. 7.15. *Typical "wet" air cleaner —an AC oil-bath unit. Passage of the air is shown by arrowed lines.*

force for dust and dirt to be trapped in the oil. Any heavier particles that fail to be caught by the oil will be filtered by the wire mesh element mounted above the oil surface.

If an engine is operated in an area where there is heavy atmospheric pollution, the oil-bath air cleaner should be serviced once a week. Release the wing nuts holding the oil-bath reservoir to the cleaner body and discard the used oil, then wipe out the container with a paraffin-soaked rag. The wire mesh element can be withdrawn and washed in petrol or paraffin oil, then immersed in clean engine oil, drained and replaced. The reservoir must be refilled with clean engine oil to the correct level, as indicated on the unit. Wipe the central intake tube clean and see that the oil bath is secure and level before finally tightening the wing nuts.

Air pre-cleaners, also called bug catchers, are fitted to some intake filters.

SUPERCHARGERS AND TURBOCHARGERS

In some two-stroke diesel engines, after the air has passed through the cleaner it enters a blower unit driven from the engine. This blower, usually of the multi-lobed type (Fig. 7.16), forces the air into the cylinders under slight

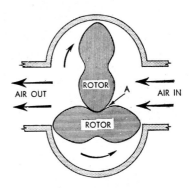

FIG. 7.16. *Action of the rotors in a blower unit for two-stroke diesel engines. Correct clearance between the rotor lobes and the casing, and between the lobes themselves as marked at A, must be maintained.*

pressure. This supercharging of the air makes a considerable difference to the efficiency of the engine. One popular unit, driven by a belt from the engine crankshaft, is illustrated in Fig. 7.17.

Superchargers of this type need occasional servicing. In particular, the clearance between the rotors must be checked, and if this is not in strict accordance with the manufacturer's specification it must be adjusted by moving the drive gears very slightly. Instructions for this exacting job are given in the engine maker's handbook.

An engine may also be fitted with a turbocharger—a small turbine driven by the exhaust gases and connected by a common shaft to an impeller-type blower (Fig. 7.18). The discharge from the impeller is connected to the intake manifold and air is delivered to the cylinders at a higher pressure,

(Above) FIG. 7.17. *B.M.C. automobile engine with Shorrock supercharger.
The unit is available for various engines.* (Below) FIG. 7.18. *Sectional views
of diesel turbochargers. On left, the C.A.V. Type O1 for engines upwards of
50 b.h.p.; on right, the Simms-Eberspacher for upwards of 80 b.h.p.*

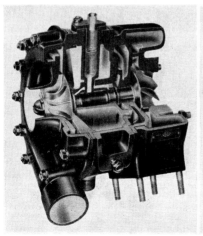

with the advantage that the power output can be increased by as much as 50 per cent, without increasing fuel consumption.

There is little to go wrong in these units, but they are very finely balanced and re-balancing of a repaired unit can only be done with the aid of expensive testing machinery. While repair is a job for experts, the only routine attention is cleaning and checking for wear in the bearings. If a turbocharger fails while at sea or on a passage between points where repairs cannot be easily affected, the best thing to do is to remove the unit and run the engine at low speed, to avoid the emission of dirty exhaust smoke from the exhaust pipe. Alternatively, the impeller can be jammed to prevent it turning, with wooden wedges fitted between the turbine blading and nozzle wheel.

EXHAUST SYSTEMS

The engine exhaust gases in a road vehicle are disposed of by passing them from the exhaust manifold through a pipe to the silencer and thence into the atmosphere. The whole system is quickly heated up by the hot gases, but does not overheat because there is a constant flow of cool air over the engine block, manifold and exhaust pipe which is drawn in by the fan. This type of exhaust system produces difficulties in a marine craft, however, where the speed is too low to permit a good flow of cool air, so that the exhaust

FIG. 7.19. *Plan view of a "wet" silencer system showing circulation of the cooling water through the cylinder block, into the exhaust manifold, thence by a separate pipe into the exhaust line.*

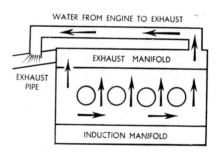

components—particularly the manifold—are in danger of becoming overheated. The marine engine's exhaust manifold is, therefore, often water-cooled, and the water thence discharged into the exhaust pipe ("wet" silencer system) to help reduce exhaust roar and cool the piping, or directly overboard ("dry" silencer system). Water drawn in from over the side is supplied to the water jacket around the manifold, as illustrated in Fig. 7.19. Examples of wet and dry silencers are shown in Fig. 7.20.

An air-cooled engine uses the more conventional exhaust system without water cooling. In this case careful planning and design is necessary to ensure that a good flow of cool air reaches all parts of the engine and its exhaust system.

Exhaust manifolds are of welded steel or cast iron. Because of the high

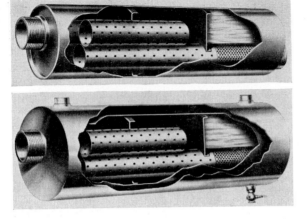

temperature at which they operate they are likely to give more trouble than intake manifolds. Occasionally the manifold will crack. This can lead to severe engine damage if the crack is on the inside of the water jacket and the water drains into the cylinders through the open exhaust valves when the engine is stopped. Trapped between piston crown and the underside of the cylinder head, the water can burst the head metal, unless the starter motor fails to crank the engine.

After a long shut-down period, if the engine has not been drained it is advisable to turn the engine over by hand before attempting to start. If it fails to turn, the sparking plugs or diesel injectors should be removed and the cylinders inspected for the presence of water. In this event, the exhaust manifold can be removed for inspection and repairs carried out before serious damage is done.

Exhaust System Installation. Fig. 7.21 shows a dry type of installation, where cooling water circulates around the exhaust manifold and is then piped overboard at a point well above the water line. Fig. 7.22 shows a wet type, where the coolant circulates around the manifold, piping and silencer

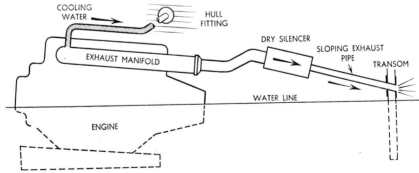

FIG. 7.21. *Circulation of cooling water in a dry silencer system.*

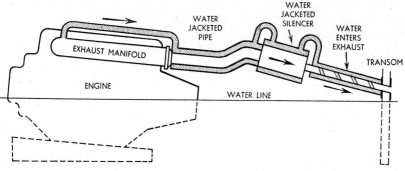

FIG. 7.22. *Circulation of cooling water in a wet silencer system.*

before being finally injected into the exhaust gas stream. There are a number of variations on these two methods.

It must be remembered that if an engine is mounted below the water line the exhaust pipe must be at least 6 in. to 8 in. above water line to avoid the risk of water backing up into the cylinders when the engine is stopped.

Exhaust lines should be kept as short as possible. This does not mean that if an engine is located amidships it should be simply led over the side at right angles to the manifold. This would be practicable, of course, but if there is an open after cockpit or accommodation abaft the beam the exhaust gases will then cause discomfort to people on board. However, exhausts of this type are not uncommon when the engine is located aft, and an excellent installation to use with this type of engine layout is shown in Fig. 7.23.

If an engine has a very loud or penetrating exhaust roar which cannot be quietened sufficiently by the silencer, it is a good plan to install a water-cooled expansion chamber to reduce the noise (Fig. 7.24). This is fitted between the silencer and the tail pipe.

Apart from keeping the exhaust line to the minimum practicable length, there should be as few bends in it as possible. These must not be severe, a bending angle of 45 deg. being far preferable to 90 deg. Very good exhaust installations can be made using the standard

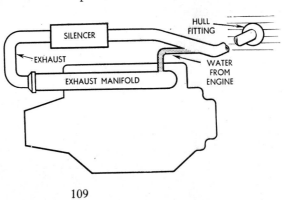

FIG. 7.23. *Exhaust system with athwartships outlet.*

pipe fittings available from ironmongers, such as 45 deg. ells, unions, couplings and reducers. The threads should be covered with a compound capable of withstanding high temperatures before the parts are screwed together.

All exhaust lines should have a length of steam metal hose or rubber steam piping between the engine and the exhaust pipe, preferably connecting

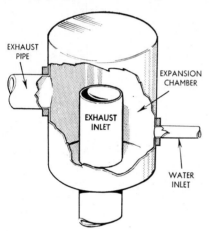

EXHAUST
PIPE

EXPANSION
CHAMBER

EXHAUST
INLET

WATER
INLET

FIG. 7.24. *Exhaust roar can be greatly reduced by fitting a water-cooled expansion chamber such as this between a dry silencer and the tail pipe. The cooling water, which may be drawn from the exhaust manifold or any convenient raw water circuit in the installation, leaves the expansion chamber with the exhaust gases.*

the manifold to the engine. This will absorb engine vibration. It need only be about 4 in. to 6 in. long and can be clipped into position. However, it cannot be jacketed.

Piping supports should be fitted so that heat from the exhaust pipe is not conducted to the boat's timbers to cause paintwork to blister and perhaps start a fire. The risk can be avoided by wrapping the section of the pipe held in the bracket in asbestos sheeting, and fitting a strip of asbestos on the base of the bracket. Asbestos rope can also be used to lag any exhaust pipes when the heat they give off interferes with comfort. The rope, or cord for small-diameter piping, is secured with a simple binding. Asbestos sleeves held in position by metal bands can also be used. They are available in almost all sizes and are quickly installed.

CHAPTER 8

Diesel Fuel Pumps

THE fuel injection pump can be regarded as the heart of the diesel engine, taking the place of both the ignition system and the carburettor of the petrol engine. It must be timed to inject the correct amount of fuel into each cylinder at the precise instant it is needed, in the same way that a petrol engine's distributor is timed to produce a spark in each cylinder at the required moment. The fuel passes into the cylinder through a spray nozzle valve which is opened by pump pressure. A typical diesel fuel system for a small craft is shown in Fig. 8.1, and a fuel injection pump in Fig. 8.2.

Most injection pumps used with modern marine diesels are of the constant-stroke, cam-actuated, lapped-plunger type. This means that the stroke of the pump (the distance the plunger travels) cannot be varied; the plunger is pushed upwards in its barrel by a cam on a camshaft in the unit, driven by the engine through gears (like cam-operated valve tappets); and the plunger is accurately ground and lapped to fit into its barrel. In many cases this grinding and lapping is carried out accurately to within one ten-thousandth of an inch—in fact, the diesel fuel pump as a whole is one of the finest pieces of precision engine equipment made for everyday work.

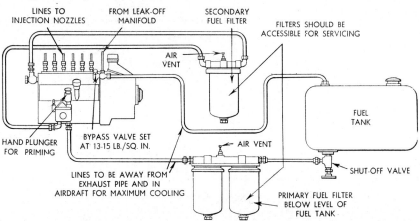

FIG. 8.1. *Typical diesel fuel system for a small craft, incorporating both primary and secondary filters. Note position of air vents.*

Although so accurately made, diesel pumps are robust and rarely go wrong if supplied with clean filtered fuel. Referring to Figs. 8.3 and 8.4 the operation of the pump is as follows:

Fuel enters the sump in the upper part of the housing as soon as the upper edge of the plunger on its downward stroke opens the ports or openings on opposite sides of the barrel. Fuel continues to enter until the plunger reaches the bottom of its stroke. Then the plunger commences to rise as the cam lifts it. Fuel is now forced out of the ports or openings until they are completely covered. Then, with tremendous force, the fuel is pushed past the delivery valve at the top of the pump and into the pipe connecting with the cylinder.

Delivery of fuel to the cylinder ends the moment the helix cut in the plunger passes the by-pass port in the barrel. The position of the helix controls the amount of fuel pumped to the cylinder. The quantity of fuel is varied by turning the plunger in its barrel, allowing the helix to match with the by-pass ports earlier or later as demanded by the engine speed.

To do this a control sleeve is slipped over the barrel. This sleeve is provided with a toothed segment which engages in the plunger, and the teeth also mesh with teeth on the control rod. On moving the control rod, by hand or governor, the plunger is rotated in its barrel. Fig. 8.5 shows the position of the helix when the plunger is set for full load, shut off, or idling.

FUEL PUMP TROUBLES

The following troubles may arise with the fuel injection pumps likely to be found on small marine diesels.

When an engine runs erratically the trouble may be caused through

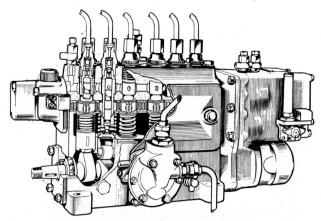

Fig. 8.2. *C.A.V. N-type fuel injection pump for high-speed diesels. This unit is fitted with a diaphragm feed pump and a mechanical governor.*

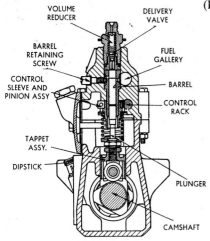

VOLUME REDUCER

DELIVERY VALVE

BARREL RETAINING SCREW

FUEL GALLERY

CONTROL SLEEVE AND PINION ASSY

BARREL

CONTROL RACK

TAPPET ASSY.

DIPSTICK

PLUNGER

CAMSHAFT

(Left) FIG. 8.3. *A Simms injection pump showing the drive from the camshaft.*

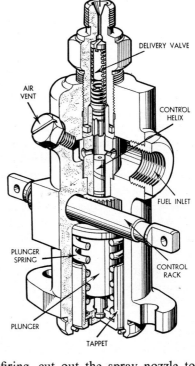

HIGH-PRESSURE FUEL DELIVERY

DELIVERY VALVE

AIR VENT

CONTROL HELIX

FUEL INLET

PLUNGER SPRING

CONTROL RACK

PLUNGER

TAPPET

(Right) FIG. 8.4. *Bryce Berger flange-mounted, constant-stroke, variable-spill injection pump for engines having their own driving cams and tappet gear.*

damage to a pump plunger or its barrel. The symptoms vary widely and can include failure to fire on one or more cylinders, failure to develop full power, low exhaust temperature and low firing pressure for the affected cylinder. To find which cylinder is misfiring, cut out the spray nozzle to each cylinder in turn. This is done by slackening back the connecting nut which attaches the high-pressure tubing to the spray nozzle.

When cutting out a particular spray nozzle has no apparent effect on the operation of the engine it is more than likely that that cylinder is misfiring. It is then necessary to dismantle the pumps, clean them thoroughly and inspect each plunger and its barrel for damage. Special cleaners are available or the parts can be soaked overnight in diesel fuel. Each plunger should be checked for the presence of possibly very fine scratches running along the top of the plunger. Sometimes the edge of the helix is corroded or nicked. If a plunger is scratched or damaged in any way it is highly desirable to return the pump to the manufacturer for complete overhaul.

Such damage usually arises from dirt or grit carried into the pump with

113

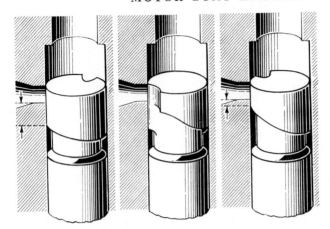

Fig. 8.5. *Positions of injection pump helix when the plunger is set for* (left to right) *full load, shut off and idling. Effective stroke of the pump is shown by the distance between the arrowheads.*

the fuel. Indeed, contaminated fuel oil is the greatest single source of trouble in injection pumps, and the fuel should be strained and filtered at least twice to ensure that no foreign matter enters the pump and causes scratches. Such scratches may appear too shallow to worry about, but as a diesel pump is such an accurate piece of equipment they can cause endless operating trouble.

When an engine misfires regularly a possible cause is external leakage of fuel. Such leakage can easily be overlooked if the engine is not kept clean and wiped down regularly. The leak can often be traced to failure to tighten the high-pressure fuel line connexions sufficiently—the slightest leak here can cause the engine to "miss".

Another cause of an engine's misfiring is the injection pump plunger sticking in its barrel for a few strokes and then breaking free. The cause will probably be found to be dirt or gummy deposits on the plunger or barrel surfaces, and again caused by dirty fuel. Very occasionally a plunger or barrel may become distorted through rough handling or even through over-tightening of the delivery valve holder. The only way of freeing a sticking plunger is to soak it in a cleaning fluid or fuel oil, then gradually work it in and out of the barrel until it slides freely into place when the barrel is held at an angle of 45 deg. A plunger or barrel which has been distorted through mishandling cannot be repaired and must be replaced.

When the speed of an engine fluctuates, or does not respond to throttle movement, sticking of the fuel control rack can be suspected. This condition should not be ignored, as quite a lot of trouble can be caused when approaching a lock or proceeding alongside if there is not instant engine response to movement of the throttle control. To check whether the control rack is at fault, disconnect the linkage between the throttle hand lever or governor and move the rack by hand. If the rack will not move easily the trouble is likely

FIG. 8.6. *Simms SPE 4A injection pump for four-cylinder engines, cut away to show working parts. This pump is fitted with a pneumatic governor, also an excess fuel device to assist cold weather starting.*

to be due to either the plunger sticking in its barrel, dirt in the rack or segment teeth, or wrong assembly of the pump. Thorough cleaning of the affected components may be all that is necessary to get the pump functioning perfectly, but if any parts are bent or damaged they will have to be replaced.

On top of the pump barrel is the delivery valve. The fuel passes through this to the engine under high pressure, being forced upwards by the rising plunger. As the plunger descends again the delivery valve closes, so that fuel cannot feed back into the pump unit. If this valve gets dirty or damaged the result will be operating trouble in the form of erratic running or break-down of the fuel supply system. If the delivery valve is adjusted at any time, the manufacturer's instructions must be closely followed because, with some types, incorrect timing will lead to the plunger striking the valve body. This in turn results in serious internal damage to the pump.

FUEL PUMP TIMING

Few single items have more to do with a marine diesel engine's efficiency than the timing of the injection pump to the engine—that is, adjusting the pump to deliver oil fuel to each cylinder at the exact moment it is required. In a diesel engine the oil fuel is injected before the piston reaches the top of its stroke. It immediately commences to burn, but a brief period of time is required for the whole of the charge to be consumed. The greater part of the fuel charge does not in fact burn until after the piston has passed the top of its stroke and begun to descend. Because of this, the injection pump must be timed to deliver fuel into each cylinder at the correct moment before the piston reaches the top of its travel. This position is measured by the amount of rotation of the crankshaft, and the normal firing position may be anywhere between 10 and 25 degrees of crankshaft rotation before the piston reaches its top dead centre.

The firing position for No. 1 cylinder is usually marked on the flywheel, and if this cylinder is timed correctly all the others will automatically be correct. The fuel pump timing is always correctly set and sealed at the factory and should never be disturbed unless it is necessary to replace the pump or some other part such as the timing gears.

When replacing an injection pump, the job should be done stage by stage as follows:

1. Clean off every trace of dirt from the pump mounting position.

2. Turn over the engine in its direction of normal rotation until No. 1 cylinder is at firing point. On most engines this is found by bringing into alignment a mark on the flywheel rim and some kind of pointer on the

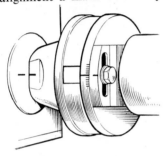

engine block. At this point the piston in No. 1 cylinder should be rising on its compression stroke, as shown by both valves being closed. Another way of checking this is to take out No. 1 spray nozzle and put a thumb over the orifice. If the engine is cranked a little it will be possible to feel the pressure of air on the thumb as the piston rises. Note that care should be taken in bringing the flywheel up to its timing mark; if it is inadvertently moved past the pointer on

FIG. 8.7. *C.A.V. fuel pump timing coupling.*

the engine block then it will have to be rotated in the opposite direction about a quarter of a full turn before being brought into alignment with the pointer again. This avoids inaccuracies due to normal running tolerances of the gears. The engine should not again be moved, but left in alignment.

3. Rotate the drive coupling on the fuel pump until the two marks on the front of the pump coupling are aligned, as in Fig. 8.7. The timing mark can also be clearly seen in Fig. 8.6.

4. Place the pump on its bracket and tighten the holding-down nuts or bolts to finger-tightness.

5. Re-align the pump coupling as accurately as possible and hold this alignment while installing the two cap screws in the two-hole coupling. The two opposite holes should be in line.

6. Tighten the holding nuts or bolts firmly and evenly. Check to ensure that the flywheel has not moved out of alignment before attempting to start the engine for a test run.

The fuel pump may not have timing marks on its coupling, in which case the "flow" method of timing will be required. The procedure is:

1. Place the flywheel in the position at which injection of the fuel should commence in No. 1 cylinder, as described above.

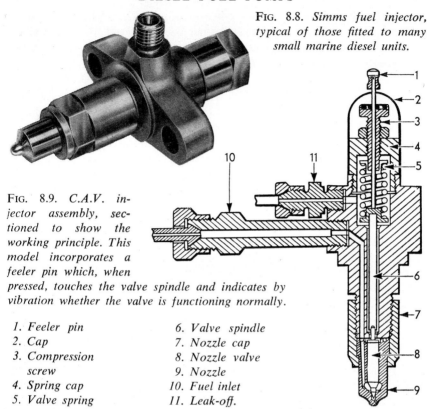

FIG. 8.8. *Simms fuel injector, typical of those fitted to many small marine diesel units.*

FIG. 8.9. *C.A.V. injector assembly, sectioned to show the working principle. This model incorporates a feeler pin which, when pressed, touches the valve spindle and indicates by vibration whether the valve is functioning normally.*

1. *Feeler pin*
2. *Cap*
3. *Compression screw*
4. *Spring cap*
5. *Valve spring*
6. *Valve spindle*
7. *Nozzle cap*
8. *Nozzle valve*
9. *Nozzle*
10. *Fuel inlet*
11. *Leak-off.*

2. Install the pump with its holding bolts or nuts but do not attach the pump coupling to the drive coupling.

3. Prime the system with the hand pump.

4. Remove No. 1 delivery valve from the injection pump.

5. Replace the throttle in the full-load position. Fuel should now rush from the pump top.

6. If the fuel does not flow again, prime the pump and keep pumping. Rotate the shaft until fuel commences to run from the pump top, then rotate it in the opposite direction until the flow of fuel is cut off. (Only a very small movement is required.)

This determines the position where the pump plunger has just closed the by-pass port and starts to build up the pressure in the line so that injection of the fuel commences in the cylinder. The operation must be carried out with great care and accuracy.

Manufacturers provide detailed instructions for their particular engines, but if the pump timing must be checked when there is no instruction book available either of the above methods can be used. The problem of retiming will not arise after an injection pump has been removed from an engine if the position of the pump coupling in relation to the drive shaft coupling is first clearly marked by means of a file cut.

SPRAY NOZZLES

The charge of fuel leaving the fuel pump delivery valve passes along a pipe and enters the cylinder head by way of a spray nozzle or injector (Fig. 8.8). This is a precision-made spring-loaded valve which allows the fuel to pass into the cylinder but prevents any combustion gas from blowing back along the pipe to the injection pump. The nozzle valve is opened by pump pressure, and it is important to keep it clean for correct working. The following are symptoms of trouble caused by dirty nozzles:

1. Black smoke in the engine exhaust.
2. Loss of power and acceleration.
3. Rough running of the engine.
4. "Knocks" from inside the combustion space.
5. Misfiring.

Nozzles should be cleaned by first soaking them in paraffin or fuel oil,

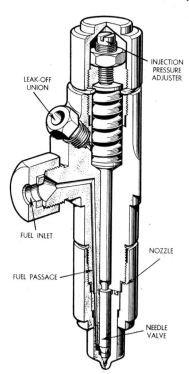

or in some proprietary brand of cleaning solvent. The interior of the nozzle body can be cleaned with a strip of wood dipped in cleaning oil and the spray holes with a pointed stick. The nozzle valve should be well rubbed with a clean oil-soaked rag. Do not use metal tools to clean the holes (unless supplied by the maker) nor emery paper to remove gummy deposits on the valve. Strainers must be removed and rinsed in clean oil before being replaced. Before assembling smear all parts with a good lubricating oil. Typical fuel injectors for marine diesels are shown in section in Figs. 8.9 and 8.10.

Spray Nozzle Testing. This can be done either with a hand-operated testing machine or by running the engine with the spray nozzle to be tested

INJECTION PRESSURE ADJUSTER

LEAK-OFF UNION

FUEL INLET

NOZZLE

FUEL PASSAGE

NEEDLE VALVE

Fig. 8.10. *Bryce Berger injector assembly.*

118

FIG. 8.11. *High-speed photograph of a typical four-hole spray pattern.*

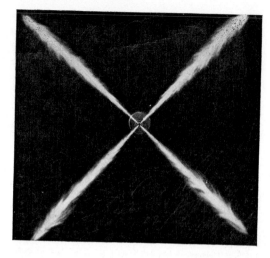

disconnected from the cylinder head. The nut attaching the connecting pipe to the injection pump is first slackened and the nozzle unit moved so that when oil is sprayed it falls clear of the engine. The connecting nut must then be retightened and the engine started.

Advance the throttle to full speed for a few moments and observe the spray pattern formed by the oil which squirts from the nozzle tip. Do not put the hand or fingers under the nozzle as the oil is discharged with sufficient pressure to puncture the skin. This is not only painful, but may lead to skin infection.

A sheet of paper placed under the spray will show the pattern quite clearly. This should normally be even and regular, without either light or dense areas. Neither should there be any "flags" showing, with too much of the oil concentrated in one area. The regular nature of the typical spray pattern is well demonstrated by high-speed photography in Fig. 8.11. In some cases the patterns are designed to be cone-shaped, and in a few others lopsided patterns are provided for specially designed combustion chambers. The cause of unevenness or distortion in the spray pattern is nearly always a dirty or obstructed nozzle hole. The hole is best cleaned with a small pointed stick and clean soft cloth.

If there is any dribble of globules of oil from the tip, the nozzle valve may not be seating correctly, allowing a small quantity of oil to escape. This must be remedied because it is a cause of heavy fuel knocks in the engine and a smoky exhaust. The unit should be exchanged or returned to the maker for overhaul.

Fuel nozzles are tested to open at very high pressures; a figure above 1,500 lb. per sq. in. is not unusual. The adjustment can be altered by turning the nut on top of the body, but this should not be attempted unless the correct testing equipment is available.

A small pump may be attached to the fuel injection pump to draw the fuel oil from the tank, deliver it through the filters and strainers and force

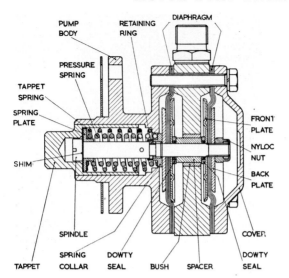

PUMP
BODY

RETAINING
RING

DIAPHRAGM

PRESSURE
SPRING

TAPPET
SPRING

SPRING
PLATE

SHIM

SPINDLE

SPRING   DOWTY
TAPPET   COLLAR   SEAL   BUSH   SPACER

FRONT
PLATE

NYLOC
NUT

BACK
PLATE

COVER

DOWTY
SEAL

FIG. 8.12. Construction of a Simms pump for forced delivery of the fuel to the injection pump unit of a diesel engine.

it into the pump casing. These feed pumps are of simple construction, as shown in Fig. 8.12, and normally give trouble only when the filters are dirty and the strainers broken. They should be overhauled whenever the injection pump is dismantled. Priming pumps are also fitted on some engines. These, too, are very simple in construction and need little attention.

For trouble-free operation of a diesel-powered craft, regular care and maintenance of the fuel oil filters and strainers is most important. These are very similar in construction and operation to those used in the lubricating oil system, and can easily be removed, cleaned and refitted (Figs. 8.13 and 8.14).

When a fuel tank has been allowed to drain dry or after an overhaul has been made, the fuel system must be primed before the engine can be expected to run satisfactorily. If the system is not primed with fuel oil there may be air present, with the result that the engine misfires, or stalls frequently, or will not start, or produces a heavy "knock".

FIG. 8.13. Vokes fuel filter with gauze and felt element, particularly suitable for primary filtration (see Fig. 8.1 for position in fuel system).

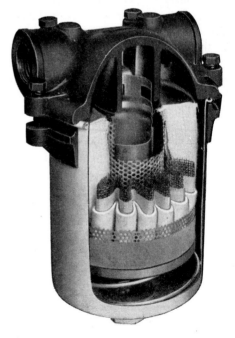

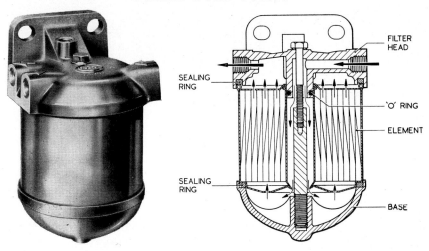

FILTER
HEAD

SEALING
RING

'O' RING

ELEMENT

SEALING
RING

BASE

FIG. 8.14. *For secondary filtration, or where only one filter is installed, the paper element type is suitable. This C.A.V. unit uses a disposable element cartridge clamped between the top and bottom castings. Direction of fuel flow is shown in the cross section.*

The presence of air in the fuel pipes can be checked by opening the bleed screw or valve on top of the fuel filter casing (if fitted) and then priming the system with the hand pump. If the fuel which runs from the vent is cloudy it contains a vast number of small air bubbles. Pumping must be continued until a stream of fuel entirely free of bubbles issues from the vent.

The piping between the injection pump and the spray nozzles must also be cleared of air. This can be done by disconnecting the line and pumping until bubble-free fuel runs from it. Then, while maintaining pressure, reconnect the line or open the bleed screw if one is provided. The injection pump, too, must be free of air, and a vent is provided for this purpose on most models.

CHAPTER 9

Electrical System

Having an elementary knowledge of what goes on in a petrol engine's electrical system will make it much easier to tackle running repairs, on-the-spot adjustments and periodical overhaul. If the engine uses coil ignition (as distinct from magneto ignition) the electrical system can be broken down into three separate circuits. These are as follows:

1. Ignition Circuit (Fig. 9.1). This provides the high-voltage spark to fire the fuel-air charge in each cylinder, and incorporates a high-tension coil, distributor and set of spark plugs. Electric current passes from the battery through the ignition switch to the high-tension coil. This unit (Fig. 9.2) contains a primary coil winding consisting of several hundred turns of comparatively thick wire, and a secondary winding consisting of thousands of turns of very fine wire. When low-voltage current from the battery passes through the primary winding, a high-voltage current can be generated by magnetic induction in the secondary winding. This secondary current cannot be induced, however, unless the primary current is switched on and off continuously and rapidly, so that surges of current flow through the primary coil winding.

This switching is the function of the contact-breaker mechanism, which is built into the distributor unit. When the pair of contact points close together, the battery circuit is completed because one terminal of the battery

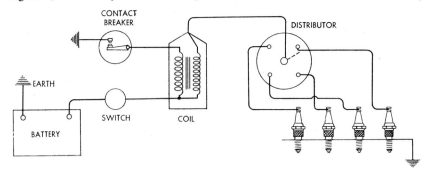

FIG. 9.1. *Basic ignition circuit of a four-cylinder petrol engine.*

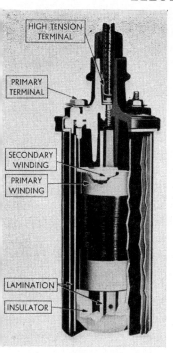

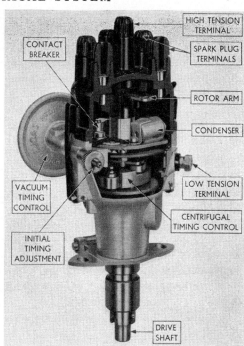

(Left) FIG. 9.2. *AC-Delco oil-filled ignition coil showing arrangement of the windings.* (Right) FIG. 9.3. *Lucas distributor for a six-cylinder engine.*

and one side of the contacts are each connected to earth. As the contact points are parted, the earth connexion is broken and the battery current ceases to flow.

A condenser or capacitor is connected across the contact points. It serves the dual purpose of preventing sparking between the contacts which would damage the points, and helping to bring about the rapid collapse of the primary current each time the contacts open; this intensifies the spark obtained at the plugs.

The high-voltage current which is induced in the secondary winding is fed through a cable to the distributor, where a rotating arm distributes it in correct sequence to each of the sparking plug cables. Each cylinder must receive its spark at exactly the right instant, when the charge of petrol-air mixture is under maximum compression. However, as it takes a brief period of time for the flame to spread through the fuel, the spark is normally set to occur just *before* the piston reaches the top of its compression stroke.

"Timing" the ignition to the cylinders, which is done by adjusting the distributor unit relative to its drive shaft, is dealt with later in this chapter.

It should be noted, however, that for greater efficiency and fuel economy the instant at which the spark occurs in the cylinder may have to be advanced or brought about earlier when the engine is running at high speeds or under light load. The modern distributor shown in section in Fig. 9.3 embodies two methods of advancing the spark under such conditions. First, there is a centrifugal governor mechanism on the drive shaft which advances the closure of the contacts (and therefore the spark) as the engine speeds up. Secondly, there is an external vacuum unit containing a diaphragm which is moved by suction from the inlet manifold. This suction is strong when the engine is running under light load, and will pull the diaphragm sufficiently to advance the closure of the contact points, as before. (The vacuum unit will not be found on older ignition systems.)

The distributor unit thus contains the contact breaker with its associated condenser, the rotor which distributes high-voltage current to all plugs, and possibly one or more means of automatically adjusting the spark timing as required. The complete mechanism is usually driven from the engine's camshaft through a skew gear.

2. Starting Circuit (Fig. 9.11). For starting the engine, current passes from the battery through the ammeter (where fitted) to the starter switch on the control panel. When the starter button is pressed and the switch closes, the current passes on to the solenoid starter unit mounted on or adjacent to the starter motor. This unit is a form of magnetic switch which closes and completes the circuit between battery and starter motor. The starter takes a very heavy current from the battery, and trouble may arise because of voltage loss if long cables are used. With a solenoid switch, only very short cables are required for the heavy starter current, the current from the starter button which actuates the solenoid mechanism being quite small. Note that in the circuit illustrated, a defective ammeter will prevent the engine being started, because current will not reach the starter button.

3. Charging Circuit (Fig. 9.4). The battery supplies current to the various items in the electrical system, but must itself be charged or supplied with current if it is not to become exhausted. It is therefore kept on charge while the engine is running by means of an engine-driven generator (or dynamo).

A cut-out switch must be interposed between the generator and the battery to break the circuit when the engine is stopped or running very slowly, otherwise current will flow back from the battery into the generator windings. This would virtually short-circuit the battery and cause damage to the generator as well. In addition, some means of controlling the voltage produced by the generator is necessary, because the voltage output varies with the speed of the machine. A voltage regulator is therefore fitted which allows the voltage to rise to a suitable level as the generator begins working and then holds it constant or adjusts it to suit the requirements of the battery.

The cut-out switch and voltage regulator are normally mounted together in one unit, which is sealed by the manufacturer and requires no attention.

Fig. 9.5 shows the principle of the "third brush" method of controlling the generator's voltage, which is used on many small marine installations. In addition to the two main carbon brushes from which the generator current is taken, there is a smaller brush connected to the regulator. Moving the position of this brush in the direction of rotation of the armature results in an increase in the voltage output; moving the brush in the opposite direction reduces the voltage. The brush is initially set by the maker for the correct output and normally should not be altered.

Fig. 9.6 shows a complete electrical system comprising the three circuits described above, and designed for a 12-volt installation. A common "earth return" is provided by connecting earthing wires to the engine metal. The ammeter and battery function in all three circuits. Fig. 9.7 shows a typical wiring diagram for a diesel engine.

The ammeter tells whether the electrical system is functioning properly or not, and every engine should be equipped with one, preferably of the centre-zero type. While the engine is idle, the ammeter needle should point to 0, or the central zero position. As the engine is switched on the needle may flutter very slightly, then fall back to zero. This movement is caused by the current passing through the ignition circuit.

While the engine is running slowly the cut-out will prevent the generator from supplying current and the ammeter should indicate that the battery is discharging a small current into the ignition circuit. As the engine speeds up and the cut-out operates, the ammeter needle should move to the "charge" side of the dial, indicating that the battery is now being supplied with current from the generator. The needle should remain on this side of the central zero position even when all lights and other electrical accessories are switched

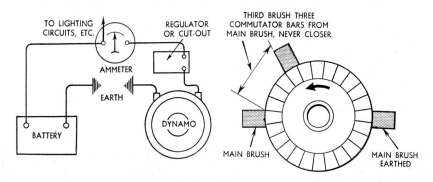

(Left) FIG. 9.4. *Basic charging circuit.* (Right) FIG. 9.5. *Third brush control of generator's output. The third brush is adjustable relative to the main brush.*

125

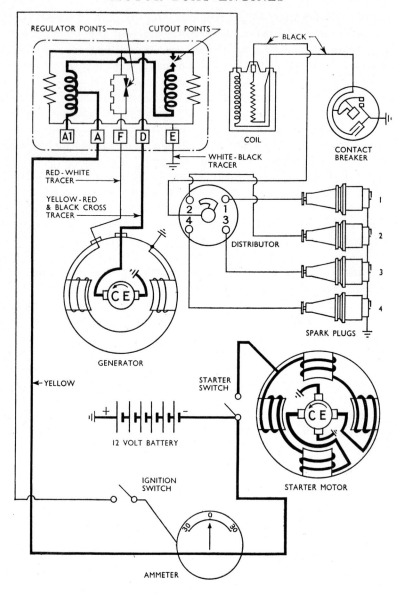

FIG. 9.6. *Typical wiring diagram for a petrol engine (Ford). The windings of the starter motor and generator are shown as viewed from the commutator end. The main cables have coloured casings to assist in identification.*

126

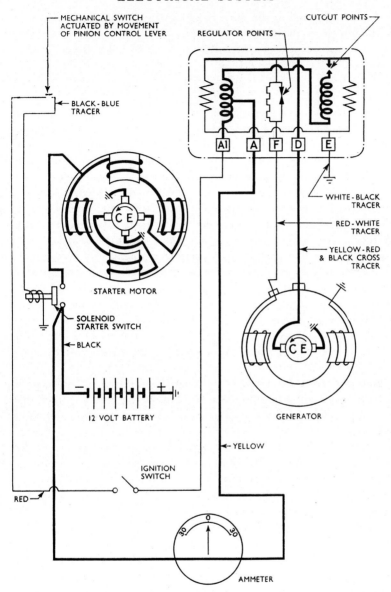

MECHANICAL SWITCH
ACTUATED BY MOVEMENT
OF PINION CONTROL LEVER

CUTOUT POINTS

REGULATOR POINTS

BLACK - BLUE
TRACER

A1 A F D E

WHITE - BLACK
TRACER

RED - WHITE
TRACER

YELLOW - RED
& BLACK CROSS
TRACER

STARTER MOTOR

C E

SOLENOID
STARTER SWITCH

BLACK

GENERATOR

C E

12 VOLT BATTERY

YELLOW

IGNITION
SWITCH

RED

30 0 30

AMMETER

FIG. 9.7. *Typical wiring diagram for a diesel engine (Ford).*

on. If it swings back to the "discharge" side of the dial, this indicates that the generator's output is insufficient to cope with the craft's full electrical load, or else the regulator unit is faulty. These troubles are dealt with later in the chapter.

ELECTRICAL FAULT-TRACING

When trouble occurs in the electrical system, it is usually fairly easy to decide whether it is the ignition, starting or charging circuit at fault. This at once narrows down the parts of the system to be checked, and a few tests in a logical sequence should quickly reveal the actual cause of the failure. Electrical trouble is often shown up at once by the engine refusing to start, but this is not always the case, and a fault such as over-charging of the battery may not be noticed for some considerable time. This is why it pays to have an ammeter fitted, and to take regular note of its reading.

Suppose that on turning the ignition switch the ammeter shows no "flick" whatever. Then either the battery is completely discharged or else the engine has stopped at a point where the contact breaker points are open. In the latter case a slight turn of the engine by hand-cranking should result in a flick of the meter needle, and the engine will be ready to start. The quickest test to discover whether there is any current at all in the battery is to press the horn button. The horn requires an appreciable amount of current, so if it sounds the battery must be at least partly charged. If not, a proper battery test should be made as described on page 135.

Ignition Circuit Troubles. If the engine turns over at sufficient speed, but does not fire when the starter button is pressed—and there is plenty of petrol in the tank—trouble may be suspected in the ignition circuit. It is true that a fault in the fuel supply system may be to blame, but ignition difficulties are more likely to be present in a marine engine because of frequent damp conditions. In addition, the ignition system can most quickly and easily be checked. If the tests described below show that this circuit is working properly, then the carburettor and other parts of the fuel system should be tested as explained in earlier chapters.

The first thing to do is to wipe dry the porcelain insulators on the sparking plugs. If there is any available, it is better to squirt a little carbon-tetrachloride (C.T.C.) on each and then wipe, because carbon-tetrachloride quickly absorbs moisture. If the engine does not start now, check the plugs.

The best way to do this is to remove each in turn, reconnect the cable, and place the plug on the engine head, making sure that the threaded body of the plug is touching bare metal on the engine block. Switch on and crank the engine a few times by hand or with the starter motor. A spark should appear between the plug's points if it is receiving its normal current.

Some owners use a screwdriver to check for sparks, placing the tip of the tool in firm contact with the engine block and then bringing the blade close to the plug terminal. When the engine is cranked a spark jumps from the terminal to the blade if the ignition circuit is in good condition. This test only proves, however, that the current is reaching the plug. It does not prove that a good-sized spark is being produced at the plug points out of sight inside the cylinder. The same objection applies to testing a plug by disconnecting its cable and holding the end within a fraction of an inch of the plug terminal.

It is wise to examine the electrodes of each plug before testing for sparks, in any case. If the points are wet or damaged, or if the gap is wrongly set, it is impossible to obtain a good spark. The same applies if the plugs are fouled with carbon or oil. Cleaning and checking of spark plugs is described later (page 139).

When a spark cannot be obtained although the plug is obviously in good condition, the cable connecting the plug with the distributor cap must be checked. It may be frayed or the wire may be broken inside the insulation. If any part of the wire is bared and making contact with the engine metal, ignition current will be lost through short-circuiting to earth before it reaches the plug. Damage to the insulation of a cable can be repaired with insulating tape or, as a temporary measure, with self-adhesive paper tape. Temporary repairs to a broken wire can be made by twisting the ends together and then taping, but damaged ignition cables should always be replaced by new ones at the earliest opportunity.

It is, of course, unlikely that all the plug cables will be damaged at the same time, so it will save time to start at the battery and check the system from there. First test from the battery to the primary circuit terminal on the

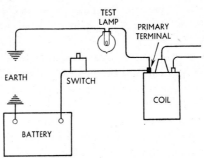

FIG. 9.8. *Testing the circuit between the battery and the primary terminal of the coil. The earth connection to the engine must be securely made.*

H.T. coil (Fig. 9.8), using a test lamp. This useful gadget is simply a holder containing a bulb (6 volts or 12 volts, depending on the battery) with two flexible insulated leads having bared ends. The sequence of operations is as follows:

1. Connect one of the test leads to any part of the engine that will provide a good earthing point, such as a bolt head. Do not use hull fittings,

but some integral part of the engine because this provides the necessary earth for the test circuit.

2. Switch on the ignition.

3. Touch the coil primary terminal with the loose lead from the test lamp. If the bulb lights up current must be reaching the coil and therefore no fault exists between the battery and the coil.

If the light in the test lamp is very dim this may indicate a loose connexion or partly earthed wire between battery and coil, in which case check for damaged insulation and loose nuts. If the lamp does not light at all this may be due to a fault in the test lamp assembly, in which case you can immediately check by touching the loose test lead to the positive (+) terminal on the battery. (The negative (−) terminal is usually earthed to the engine by a heavy metal strap.) The lamp will light if the test assembly is working properly.

If no light is obtained, and a check shows that the test lamp assembly is in order, the fault may lie in the ignition switch. Touch the test lead to the switch terminal on the side closest to the battery; if the lamp lights, the cable from battery to switch is in order. Next, touch the terminal on the coil side of the switch, ensuring that the switch is still "on". If the lamp does not light the switch must be defective. As a further check, connect one lead of the test lamp to the battery positive terminal and the other to the primary terminal on the H.T. coil, so that the ignition switch is "by-passed", and press the engine starter button. If the engine fires this finally proves that the ignition switch is at fault.

As a temporary measure one can run a piece of cable from the battery positive to the coil terminal and so cut out the broken switch. For such temporary electrical repairs it is useful to keep on board a "jumper", consisting of a length of insulated wire with a crocodile clip fitted at each end.

A jumper wire can also be used when the ignition key has been lost. If there is insufficient cable available to run from the battery to the coil, the same result can be obtained by connecting the two terminals on the defective switch together with a short length of wire.

Assuming that the circuit proves to be in order up to this point, the next item to be checked is the connexion between the coil and the distributor —not the high-tension cable leading from the top of the coil but the thinner lead which connects the primary of the coil with the contact breaker(Fig.9.9). Connect one lead of the test lamp to this primary coil terminal and the other to earth. Now crank the engine. If the lamp flashes on and off the primary circuit must be sound and the contact breaker is working satisfactorily. If the test lamp remains alight instead of flashing on and off one possible cause is a defective wire between the coil and the contact breaker. In this case a jumper lead can be connected temporarily between the two terminals.

FIG. 9.9. *Testing primary circuit of the coil and the lead to the contact breaker. The test lamp is connected in turn to points A and B, as explained in the text.*

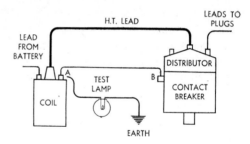

A more likely reason for the test lamp staying alight, however, is trouble at the contact breaker points—particularly from dirty or oily contacts. To check the contact breaker, first switch off the engine. Lift off the distributor cap, which has spring clips, crank the engine and observe the contact breaker points. If these do not open, the spring is either broken or else, due to arcing, a contact has been built up between the two points, preventing them breaking apart at the required moment. The parts concerned can be seen in the distributor shown in Fig. 9.10.

If the spring is broken and another is not available a temporary expedient is to use a length of elastic, hooking it around the metal arm to which the moving point is attached, and from there across the distributor to the condenser nut on the opposite side. It is fixed to the nut by twisting it around a few times. Fixing the elastic will involve removing the contact breaker unit from its base after taking out the centre screw.

Using a piece of elastic like this should get the craft home. On a long run it will probably have to be replaced once or twice, but it enables the engine to keep running. Do not use metal springs for this purpose, however.

If the carbon points are sticking or fouled they can be cleaned by gentle rubbing with a fine file or sandpaper. The minimum of filing is desirable, and the two faces must be finished dead flat and parallel. If the points are badly burned they will have to be replaced.

Assuming that the points are in good condition and the spring is not broken, contact breaker trouble will probably be due to a faulty condenser—although condenser breakdown is often shown by excessive burning of the contact points. To check, disconnect the insulated terminal of the condenser and see whether the engine will now start. If so, there is an open circuit in the condenser. If the test lamp remains alight irrespective of whether the contact points are open or closed—and the condenser is in circuit—there is a short circuit in the component. In either case, a new condenser will be required. An engine can be operated without a condenser, but only for a short time as the points will soon burn out and need frequent redressing. A burned-out condenser is not repairable, but in emergency it would be possible to substitute a radio-type condenser of 0.005 mfd. capacity. This might have

131

to hang outside the distributor casing on long wires, but it would allow the boat to get home without burning the contact points or breaking down.

If the contact breaker is working satisfactorily, the next thing to check is the high-tension circuit, which supplies the high-voltage ignition current to the sparking plugs. To do this, disconnect the cable from the top of the

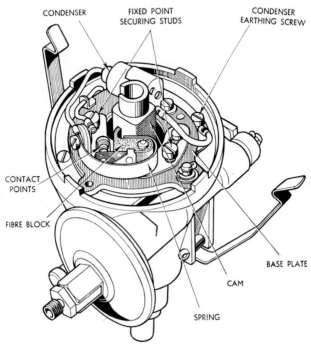

FIG. 9.10. *Assembly of the parts in a typical contact breaker unit of a distributor. The mechanism seen below the contact breaker is the vacuum timing control.*

distributor cap and fasten it to the engine block so that there is about ⅛ in. clearance between the bared end of the cable and the engine metal. This is best done by inserting a strip of wood between the cable and cylinder block and securing at two points with insulating tape. Switch on the ignition and hand-crank the engine. If a strong white spark jumps the gap this indicates that the H.T. coil is in sound condition. Absence of a spark indicates a fault in the coil, in which case a new coil will have to be obtained, as repairs are impracticable.

If the coil is good, the last item to be checked is the distributor rotor arm. This can usually be lifted vertically off its boss for inspection. If the metal strip is burned, gently rub off the marks with sandpaper, then refit the rotor arm. Check that the spring-loaded carbon connector at the end of the H.T.

cable from the coil will move freely in its socket and make proper contact with the rotor arm. Ensure that the cables to the plugs each make a sound connexion in the distributor cap and are not crossed over.

Occasionally a short circuit develops in the distributor through arcing, as shown by carbon burn marks. A temporary repair can be made by scraping away the area around the burn marks and filling the burned-out depression with rubber solution of the kind used for repairing bicycle punctures. This will not work for long, but may last long enough to get the craft home.

Starter Circuit Troubles. By far the likeliest fault to be found in connexion with starting is a "flat" battery. A heavy electrical load is imposed on the battery by the starter motor, especially when the engine is cold, and if the battery is discharged it cannot turn over the starter fast enough to make the engine fire. If the starter does not function or only turns over very slowly, therefore, the first thing to check is the battery. This can be done by simply pressing the horn button, as already mentioned; by connecting a test lamp between its terminals; by measuring the voltage across the terminals with a voltmeter; or by the use of a hydrometer as explained later. If there is a little current left in the battery, hand-cranking may get the engine to fire. If the battery is shown to be completely dead, however, cranking will be useless.

To get over this difficulty a number of flashlight batteries can be wired together in series (that is, negative to positive), making a battery pack which will give 6 volts or 12 volts as required. One of the end terminals of the pack must be fastened to the engine metal; this will be the earthed side of the battery. The cable between the ignition switch and the H.T. coil primary terminal should then be disconnected at the switch and hooked up to the other end terminal of the battery pack. The temporary battery will then feed a small current through the coil to the sparking plugs, and hand-cranking should start the engine.

Another method is to obtain a car battery of the same voltage and use this to get the engine started while the craft is lying alongside. Using jumper leads, the car battery's negative ($-$) terminal is connected to the negative terminal of the starter battery. The two positive terminals are also connected together. All connexions must be clean and tight. With the two batteries thus connected in parallel, the engine should fire when the starter button is pressed. As soon as the engine is running normally the jumper leads can be removed and the car battery taken away.

If an engine will not crank although the battery is known to be fully charged, the first check should be made at the starter switch. Attach a short jumper wire from the starter switch to the battery, then switch on. If the engine now cranks there must be a fault in the cable between the battery and the starter switch. If nothing happens, by-pass the starter switch by extending the jumper lead to run from the battery to the solenoid terminal

(Fig. 9.11). If the engine now cranks either the starter switch itself or else the wiring between it and the solenoid is defective.

Supposing the starter will not operate, the next step is to make a connector with heavy-gauge cable and connect this between the positive terminal of the battery and the starter motor terminal, thus by-passing the solenoid. Care must be taken not to touch the engine metal with the bare end when making the connexion as severe arcing can be caused. If the engine now

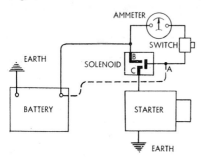

FIG. 9.11. *Starting circuit. Current must reach point A for the solenoid to switch the current from B to C. A fault in the circuit between the battery and solenoid can be by-passed by a temporary lead (shown dotted).*

cranks the trouble must lie in the solenoid. (It is useful to know that most starter solenoids can be operated manually when necessary, by pressing the plunger switch inwards; the plunger is usually protected by a rubber cap.)

If the starter motor will not operate although current is proved to be reaching it, the next step is to connect the leads of a voltmeter across the battery terminals and press the starter button. If the meter shows a drop in the voltage of only one volt there is a break (open circuit) in the windings of the starter motor. Such damage can be repaired only by specialists.

If the voltage drops by more than one volt then in all probability the Bendix starter drive is jammed against the flywheel ring gear. To free it, hand-crank the engine. If this does not release the drive, slacken back the starter holding nuts a few turns and give the unit a good shake. This should move the binding gear.

To test a starter motor, remove it from the engine and connect it to a fully charged battery. If it will not run at a regular, normal speed the unit should be sent back to the makers or an electrical service depot for overhaul. If all that is wrong is the commutator gear, however—worn or dirty carbon brushes, dirty or greasy commutator face, weak brush springs, etc.—it is not difficult to dismantle the motor and clean and adjust these parts, as described later (page 141). Commutator trouble will usually be evidenced by sparking at the brushes.

When an engine will turn over with the starter in operation, but only very slowly, likely causes are low battery charge, loose connexions between battery and starter, or a dirty solenoid.

Charging Circuit Troubles. If the generator (or dynamo) is not in good condition the battery cannot be expected to provide starting and ignition current for any length of time. The efficiency of the generator can be roughly gauged from the ammeter. When the engine has been running for a few minutes at a speed above its idling rate the ammeter needle should point towards the "charge" mark. If the lights or radio are then switched on the reading should be reduced.

When the battery charge is always low there is likely to be a fault in either the generator or the regulator. The following test can be made to decide where the trouble lies.

Disconnect the generator-to-regulator leads, taking care they do not make contact, and run the engine at the speed—a little above idling—at which the ammeter would normally show a "charge" reading. Touch the generator field-coil lead to the armature terminal on the voltage regulator. The ammeter should immediately show a reading on the "charge" side of the dial.

Should the ammeter record a "charge" reading while the field-coil lead is disconnected there is a defect in the wiring between the regulator and the generator—it is touching "earth" metal. On the other hand, if the generator does not show any output when the armature terminal is touched with the field-coil lead the regulator is defective.

Regulators can only be repaired by experts. However, when a regulator is defective the craft can be used for a short time by wedging the moving contact strip of the armature against the fixed strip, so that the points remain closed. The regulator might possibly burn out and be damaged beyond repair, and the battery could then overheat, but if the craft *must* be got moving despite a defective regulator this is one way to do it. In such a case the engine should be operated at little more than idling speed.

As well as failing to charge a battery to the full amount, generators can overcharge them. An excessively high charging rate is shown by lamp bulbs burning out after short service, the contact-breaker points burning and needing frequent re-dressing, and the electrolyte in the battery quickly falling below the level of the plates, so that constant topping-up is necessary. Overcharging trouble is generally due to the regulator, and it is simplest to replace the unit rather than attempt to adjust it.

GENERAL ELECTRICAL MAINTENANCE

Batteries. Some reference to rapid methods of battery testing has already been made under "Fault-tracing". Regular care of this unit is essential if the battery is to give efficient service and have a reasonably long life—a neglected battery soon becomes useless. However, maintenance is quite easy.

The ordinary lead-acid type of battery (Fig. 9.12) is made up of several separate 2-volt cells, mounted in a moulded case and linked together so as to provide a total electrical output of 6 or 12 volts. Apart from the positive and negative plates, each cell contains a mixture of sulphuric acid and distilled water, called the electrolyte. A filler plug is provided on each cell to allow for checking and refilling with electrolyte, and for making hydrometer tests to indicate whether the battery is charged or not. A small amount of hydrogen gas is liable to be generated when a charging current is passing through the electrolyte, which could build up internal pressure. The cell plugs therefore have vent holes which must be kept clear.

It is a good idea to check the electrical output and general condition of the battery weekly, or at least once a fortnight. A voltmeter will indicate whether 6 volts or 12 volts are available at the battery terminals, but unless a special "discharge test" meter unit is used, this test will not show what is the voltage when there is a heavy load on the battery, as when the starter is being operated. A better test is to measure the specific gravity (s.g.) of the electrolyte, which varies according to the state of electrical charge. This can easily be done with a hydrometer, an instrument costing only a few shillings.

To use the hydrometer, take off a battery filler plug, insert the instrument's rubber tube, then squeeze the bulb so that a quantity of electrolyte will be drawn up into the glass body. Just enough electrolyte is required to lift the inner float off the bottom. If the hydrometer is then held vertically at eye level, the reading on the float scale at the surface level of the electrolyte can be taken (Fig. 9.13).

The reading obtained will vary according to the air temperature as well as the state of charge. The following table shows the readings for a Lucas battery and may be used as a general guide (other battery manufacturers may quote slightly different figures for their products and those figures should then be used). Note that the specific gravity of the electrolyte in the cells should be within 0.005 above or 0.010 below the values given.

Air Temperature deg. F.	Specific Gravity		
	Fully Charged	Half Discharged	Fully Discharged
50	1·288	1·208	1·118
60	1·284	1·204	1·114
70	1·280	1·200	1·110
80	1·276	1·196	1·106

Check each cell in the same way; there should be similar readings at all of them. If one cell gives a markedly different reading, this is a sign of trouble and the unit should be replaced or overhauled by battery specialists.

If there is insufficient electrolyte in the cells to allow a hydrometer test

 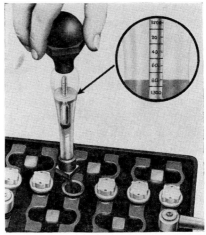

(Left) FIG. 9.12. *A modern 12-volt battery cut away to show cell construction. Speedy topping-up is provided by a one-piece cover incorporating plugs for the filler holes.* (Right) FIG. 9.13. *Using a hydrometer to test the state of charge.*

to be made, the battery will first have to be topped-up with distilled water. Electrolyte should always be kept at least $\frac{1}{8}$ in. above the tops of the plates, the exact level for each battery being specified by the manufacturer or marked on the casing. If no distilled water is available, freshly caught rain-water can be used instead, but do not put in mains water as this often contains injurious salts. Do not attempt to make a hydrometer test immediately after topping-up with water, but first run the engine at a fast idling speed for about 30 minutes, so that the charging current will mix the acid and water together.

Never top-up the battery with acid. Fresh sulphuric acid will be required only if the electrolyte is spilled or otherwise lost, and then it is best to turn the job over to mechanics with experience of battery work. Although diluted, the sulphuric acid used in a battery can burn the skin, destroy cloth and damage paintwork and metals. The battery must therefore be well stowed so that it cannot overturn or come adrift. It should be well ventilated, and preferably mounted on a properly designed battery tray which will catch any spillage of electrolyte. The terminals and holding-down bolts on the battery should be kept coated with petroleum jelly or one of the proprietary anti-corrosion greases, and the surrounding wood and metal work should be painted with acid-resisting compound. Incidentally, spilt sulphuric acid can be neutralised by simply applying diluted ordinary household ammonia or a soda solution.

Unless the proper precautions are taken corrosion will soon become a problem. It usually appears as a white or yellowish flaky encrustation on the terminals and other metal parts. Affected parts should be cleaned thoroughly with dilute ammonia, then coated with petroleum jelly or other anti-corrosive agent. Corrosion may be a sign of excessive electrolyte in the cells, of overcharging, or of allowing the battery to become wet.

Other battery troubles are sulphation and the breaking away of paste from the plates. Either can lead to the formation of sediment at the bottom of the cells, eventually short-circuiting the plates. There are several possible causes of sulphation. Sometimes an overhaul by specialists can make a sulphated battery fit for further service but in general it is probably sounder policy to scrap it and install a new one.

Some craft are fitted with nickel-alkaline batteries, whose construction is somewhat different from the lead-acid type. Each cell gives 1.2 volts instead of 2 volts, so more cells are required to make up a 6-volt or 12-volt battery. These units are thus larger and also more expensive than lead-acid batteries. On the other hand, the battery has a long life, it can be completely discharged without risk of damage to the cells, sulphation cannot occur, the alkaline electrolyte used is non-corrosive, and when necessary it is possible to charge the battery very rapidly with a heavy charging current. Practically the only maintenance needed by nickel-alkaline batteries is topping-up with distilled water, this being required rather more frequently than in the case of lead-acid units.

Sparking Plugs. The performance of the plugs has a considerable effect on an engine, and it is essential that only the type of plug specified by the engine manufacturer be used.

There are three main types of sparking plug available for different petrol engines, and these are illustrated in Fig. 9.14. They are the *hot* or *soft* type,

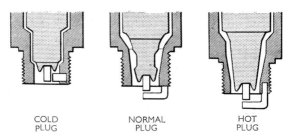

COLD PLUG   NORMAL PLUG   HOT PLUG

FIG. 9.14. *Insulator design of the three main types of sparking plug.*

for use in cool-running engines, with a long insulator which keeps hot enough to burn off oil and carbon deposits. Secondly, there is the *cold* or *hard* type, for use in certain high-efficiency engines, with a shorter insulator which is more rapidly cooled. The *normal* type comes between the first two. A cold

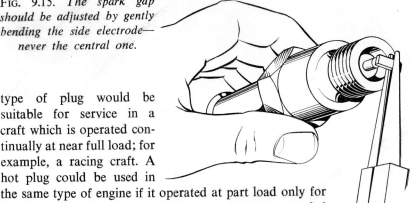

FIG. 9.15. *The spark gap should be adjusted by gently bending the side electrode— never the central one.*

type of plug would be suitable for service in a craft which is operated continually at near full load; for example, a racing craft. A hot plug could be used in the same type of engine if it operated at part load only for long periods, while a normal plug can be recommended for an engine chiefly operating at intermediate speeds.

Some sparking plugs can be dismantled for cleaning purposes; others are of one-piece construction. In either case, regular examination, cleaning, and spark-gap adjustment is essential for good running. The correct servicing procedure is to disconnect the ignition cable, slacken back the plug two or three turns only and then brush or wipe away all loose dirt and rust around it; otherwise this dirt will get into the cylinder when the plug is taken out. Next, remove the plug together with any gasket or joint washer and check the condition of the points and insulator.

Cleaning of the metal portion can be carried out with a wire scratch brush, the faces of the points can be rubbed over gently with a fine-cut file or emery cloth, and the porcelain insulator can be washed in petrol. If the interior of the plug is fouled with oil, some petrol can be poured in and ignited, the plug being held in pliers while the oil is burned away. After cleaning, the points gap must be checked with a feeler gauge and reset, if necessary, to the dimension specified by the engine manufacturer. Adjustment must be made by bending the side (earth) electrode—not the centre electrode (Fig. 9.15).

Before refitting the plug, its outside should be thoroughly cleaned as any dirt or grease may provide a path to earth for high-voltage ignition current, leading to "tracking" and loss of spark. Do not overlook the gasket washers, and replace these by new ones if they are cracked or badly flattened, because they provide the essential gas-tight seal for the combustion chamber. The plug should be screwed down sufficiently to compress the gasket to about half its original thickness. Excessive tightening may cause the body to distort and the porcelain to crack. On the other hand, if the plug is too loose combustion gas may escape around the threads, which will become overheated and burnt.

| Oily deposits are a likely sign of worn piston rings or poor sparking conditions. | Sooting-up of the insulator may indicate that too rich a fuel mixture is being used. | Worn points result from excessively hot running, and call for a cooler working plug. |

| Corroded threads indicate that hot combustion gases are escaping around the plug. | Fue deposits are left by modern additives and should be cleaned off regularly. | Pre-ignition is shown by whiteness, more or less speckled, of the insulator tip. |

FIG. 9.16. *Examination of the "business end" of each sparking plug can provide useful information on ignition conditions.*

As mentioned above, the points and insulator should be examined carefully before they are cleaned, as a good deal can be learned from their condition (Fig. 9.16). If they are coated by a dry, light to dark brown, flaky deposit this is an indication of good combustion conditions within the cylinder. If the plug has been overheated this may be shown by dry, shiny or glassy deposits on the insulator and by cracks in the insulation around the tip. Overheating of plugs can be caused by:

1. Too lean a fuel mixture, i.e. insufficient petrol in the incoming air.
2. Inefficient engine cooling.
3. Broken or slipping fan belt.
4. Too hot a spark for the type of service in which the craft is engaged (i.e., wrong type of plug).
5. Faulty insulation on the plug.
6. Compression leakage past the plug, due to stripped threads on the plug base or in the cylinder head, or to the plug having been inserted incorrectly or not tightened sufficiently.

If plug points are found to be covered by a dry, black, fluffy deposit the cause may be one of the following:

1. The plug is of the wrong type and too cold for the particular service that the craft is engaged in.

2. The engine has idled for long periods.

3. Excessive use of the choke or improper adjustment of the choke if of the automatic type.

4. Too rich a fuel mixture, i.e., excessive petrol in the incoming air.

5. Spark plug gap is too small.

If the points and insulators are coated with a wet, shiny deposit the trouble is due to oil getting on to the plug. Possible causes are :

1. The plug is too cold for the service in which the boat is engaged.

2. The distributor is not functioning correctly or the ignition system generally needs overhauling.

3. Battery is weak or the H.T. coil faulty.

4. Spark plug gap is too small.

5. Piston rings are worn.

6. Worn oil seals on the valve stems.

Sparking plugs will not wear for ever. The points become eroded with service and it is then impossible to set the gap correctly or obtain a good spark. When this becomes apparent it is best to fit a complete set of new plugs.

Generators and Starter Motors. These are very similar in construction, and similar maintenance methods apply. The armature windings and magnetic parts require no attention whatever. Most modern starters have permanently lubricated bearings which require no attention, but the small engine-driven generator usually has a lubricator for its rear bearing, in

FIG. 9.17. *Main components of the Siba Dynastart combined starter motor and 12 - volt generator unit.* Top left to bottom right: *arma-ture assembly, switch assembly box with condenser, contact breaker and fixed cam, ignition coil, stator assembly.*

FIG. 9.18. *Lucas "pre - engaged" starter motor. In this type, engagement of the driving pinion with the engine flywheel is made before the motor starts to turn.*

FIELD COILS | PILOT SWITCH | ENGAGING LEVER | COMMUTATOR | ARMATURE | CLUTCH ASSEMBLY | DRIVING PINION

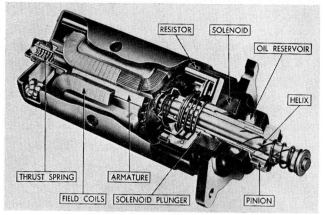

RESISTOR | SOLENOID | OIL RESERVOIR | HELIX | THRUST SPRING | ARMATURE | FIELD COILS | SOLENOID PLUNGER | PINION

FIG. 9.19. *C.A.V. co-axial starter, designed mainly for light diesels. The pinion is moved into engagement by a solenoid and locked mechanically until the starter button is released.*

FIG. 9.20. *Simms inertia starter. Energy from handcranking is built up in a small flywheel and transferred to the engine by operating a clutch. The unit is suitable for diesel engines of up to about six litres.*

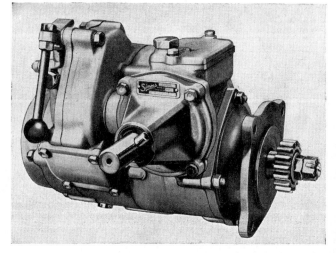

which a few drops of oil must be injected at regular intervals. The small self-contained generating sets require very little attention over a long running period, and are supplied with maintenance instructions from the maker.

A typical starter motor with drive gear is illustrated in Fig. 9.18. Another type, intended mainly for use with light diesel engines, is shown in Fig. 9.19. This has a built-in solenoid which causes the piston to engage with the flywheel as soon as the starter button is pressed, and before full power is developed. This two-stage arrangement reduces wear on the gear teeth and enables the starter power to be applied more smoothly. Fig. 9.20 shows an inertia-type starter, useful for hand-cranking petrol and diesel engines. A hand crank is attached to the shaft in the centre of the unit and when turned this causes a small flywheel to revolve at high speed. A clutch is then operated by the handle on the left and this transfers the energy stored in the flywheel to the starter pinion on the right.

A rather different sort of starter motor, with which several outboard engines are fitted, is the Siba Dynastart. As its name implies, this equipment is a combined starter and generator, forming a compact unit which is incorporated in the engine. The component units of the Dynastart are shown in Fig. 9.17.

A typical small generator is shown in Fig. 9.21. The main attention required both for generators of this type and for small motors generally is

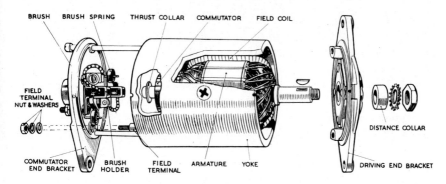

FIG. 9.21. *Components of a typical small generator* (*Lucas*).

maintenance of the copper-faced commutator ring and its associated carbon pick-up brushes. Servicing procedure is as follows:

1. Remove the cover band over the body or unscrew the through-bolts and dismantle the armature, as appropriate. Examine the commutator faces, which should have a coppery sheen, without black marks or scratches. Lift the brush holder springs and check that they snap back into place. If these

are broken or too weak to press the brushes into contact with the commutator they will have to be renewed.

2. Check the carbon brushes for freedom of movement. They should
move without sticking but not too loosely when the pigtail leads are pulled.
If the brushes stick they should be removed and cleaned on a sheet of
sandpaper spread on a flat surface. A few rubs on all surfaces except the
bottom one should ease the brush sufficiently. Sticking of brushes is often
due to over-lubrication of the generator bearing, with oil getting on to the
armature.

3. If the brushes are worn down too far to make proper contact with
the commutator face they must be replaced. A new brush has a square end
and this will have to be bedded or shaped to the exact contour of the
commutator surface. This can be done by wrapping a length of fine-grade
sandpaper over the commutator, placing the brush in position and slowly

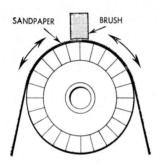

FIG. 9.22. *Bedding-in the
generator's carbon brushes by
see-sawing a strip of sandpaper
face upwards over the bars
of the commutator.*

but firmly working the sandpaper up and down as shown in Fig. 9.22.
Alternatively, wrap the paper over the commutator and turn the armature
slowly. Unless the new brush seats properly against the commutator, arcing
and burning of the brushes will result, due to the heavy current load on a
very small contact area.

4. If the copper faces of the commutator ring are greasy or dirty, it may
be sufficient to press a piece of cloth moistened in petrol against them and
turn the armature round two or three times. If this proves insufficient to
clean the faces, wrap a piece of fine-grade sandpaper over a sliver of wood,
press this against the commutator and again rotate the armature. (Never use
emery cloth for this job as the copper faces will be badly scratched.) When
a bright, shining surface free from all marks has been restored, all copper
dust must be wiped or blown away from the commutator because it can
cause short-circuiting between segments.

The commutator bars are insulated from each other by thin mica strips,
and these must be kept about 1/32 in. below the face of the bars to avoid
sparking at the commutator (Fig. 9.23). After cleaning the commutator face,

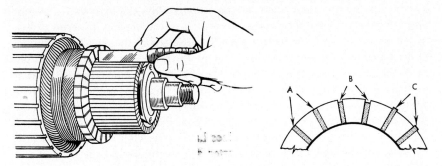

FIG. 9.23. *A knife blade is used to undercut the mica insulating strips between commutator bars, giving the effect shown on the right at B. A level face, as at A, or raised mica strips as at C, both need attention.*

therefore, the grooves between the bars may have to be undercut to the correct depth, and this can be done by drawing a knife blade or short length of hacksaw blade along each groove. The grooves are often choked with carbon dust caused by the brushes wearing down, and this must be cleaned or blown away before the unit is re-assembled.

Ignition Timing. In the previous chapter it was explained that a fuel injection pump has to be "timed" to a diesel engine, so that oil is sprayed into the cylinder as the piston rises to the top of its compression stroke. Similarly, in a petrol engine the distributor must be timed or set so that the spark occurs at each sparking plug as the piston reaches the top of its compression stroke. Normally the distributor setting will need no attention, but if ever the unit is taken off during overhaul and the crankshaft is moved, retiming will be necessary when the distributor is replaced.

Directions for timing the distributor are usually given in the engine maker's instruction book, and these should be followed closely. If no instructions for a particular engine are available, however, the following method gives reasonably accurate results.

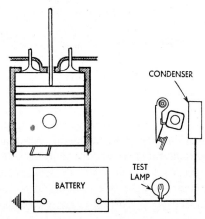

FIG. 9.24. *Timing an engine with a test lamp connected between battery and condenser. Top dead centre of the piston stroke is found by inserting a rod in the sparking plug hole.*

145

The distributor is installed but not finally clamped in position. A test lamp of either 6 volts or 12 volts, according to the engine concerned, must be connected between the battery supply terminal and the insulated terminal on the condenser, as shown in Fig. 9.24. With the ignition switch turned off, crank the engine slowly and observe the test lamp. As the contact breaker points close the lamp will light; it should go out again as the points open. Having checked this, it will now be necessary to find top dead centre on the compression stroke of No. 1 piston.

To locate this position, most engines have some kind of timing indicator or marks on the flywheel face or starter gear teeth around the rim, or else at the front of the engine on the crankshaft pulley or camshaft gear. Common forms of indicator are a scribed mark on the flywheel which can be aligned with an aperture in the flywheel housing; a steel ball fitted into the flywheel face to line up with a groove in the housing; and a notch cut in the rim of the crankshaft pulley to align with an indicator on the front timing cover; while certain small Ford engines much used in small craft have a detachable pin in the timing cover which engages with a "dimple" in the camshaft sprocket. Whatever form they take, the timing marks must be brought approximately into alignment; the piston in No. 1 cylinder will now be about the top of its compression stroke.

Now remove the sparking plug from No. 1 cylinder (nearest the front of the engine) and put a pencil, thin ruler or other length of wood into the hole so that it rests on the piston crown. Turning the hand crank a very small amount either way will raise the pencil to its highest point—i.e., will bring No. 1 piston to top dead centre. The sparking plug should fire just as the piston reaches this position, as shown by the test lamp lighting up.

If the lamp indicates that the spark is occurring too soon or too late, adjustment is made by rotating the distributor body slightly one way or the other. When the lamp indicates that the plug will fire just as the piston reaches top dead centre, the distributor can be locked in position by means of its clamp bolt.

Magnetos. Many small marine engines are equipped with a magneto instead of coil ignition. The magneto contains a transformer to produce the high-voltage ignition current (instead of an H.T. coil), and also a generator which produces the low-voltage primary supply when driven by the engine. Thus, the magneto has the advantage that it produces its own electrical power and needs no battery. On the other hand, its output voltage will vary with the speed of the engine. A good strong spark is produced at the higher speeds, but performance may be affected a good deal at idling speeds. The magneto is used solely to produce ignition current, a battery or generator being installed if lighting and other electrical facilities are required.

The H.T. current is taken to the plugs through a distributor, which may have automatic timing mechanism as in a coil-ignition distributor. A contact breaker and condenser are also incorporated. When the engine is switched off the primary current is connected through the switch to earth, and this short-circuits the contact breaker so that the H.T. current is immediately cut off.

Fig. 9.25 is a sectioned view of a vertical type of magneto, driven at half engine speed from the engine camshaft like an ordinary distributor. Horizontal magnetos are also in use, the generating mechanism being driven at

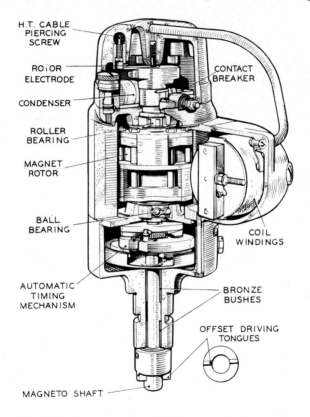

FIG. 9.25. *Cut-away view of a Lucas vertical magneto.*

engine speed, while the distributor is geared down to half engine speed. Outboard engines, and some inboard engines of the two-stroke type, use a flywheel magneto (Fig. 9.26).

Most of the fault-tracing methods already described for coil-ignition systems are equally applicable to magneto systems. Vertical magnetos have a lubricator for the armature bearings, whereas horizontal magnetos usually

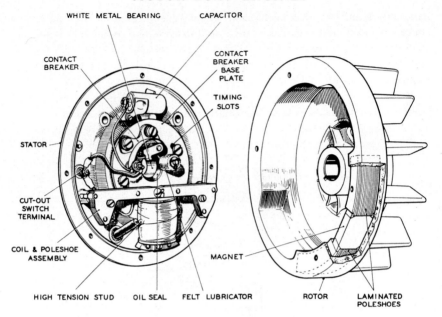

FIG. 9.26. *Component parts of a Lucas flywheel magneto. Ignition advance is adjusted by rotating the contact breaker assembly on the timing slots.*

have bearings sealed with lubricant which require attention only at very long intervals. Distributor lubrication is the same as for coil-ignition units, and on most modern magnetos the contact breaker is very similar to those used with coil ignition, requiring cleaning and gap-setting in the same way.

LIGHTING INSTALLATION AND MAINTENANCE

Electric lighting in a boat should not be any problem if the battery is sufficiently powerful to supply the needed current. In many cases the engine electrical system of a new boat is designed to provide the necessary ignition current and starting power with sufficient to spare for two or three lamps. As time passes other lamps (Figs. 9.27 and 9.28) are added together with other electrical accessories such as a motor-driven ventilating fan. The eventual result of adding such equipment is that the battery is unable to provide all the current required and starting becomes more and more difficult as the engine fails to obtain proper cranking speed.

Batteries are fitted to small craft to supply the engine and instrument lighting as well as current for the dashboard, navigation and two or three cabin lights. The normal charging system is not intended to deal with any greater drain on the electrical supply, and where additional power is required the proper answer is to install a separate generating set, or additional batteries which can be removed from the boat for charging ashore. Too often, however, extra lamps and similar items are simply wired up between any likely-looking live point and some piece of boat ware more or less in contact with the main electrical earth.

It is a good idea to get rid of this type of "Christmas tree" installation in any craft, and essential if the power supply is being persistently overloaded. In planning a new installation it will first be necessary to work out what will be the total consumption of power when all the electrical items are operating. This can be found by adding together the wattages for the separate items. For example:

4 navigation lamps, 18 watts each		72 watts
6 cabin lights, 12 watts each	...	72 watts
Wireless set, 30 watts ...	...	30 watts
8 small lamps, 3 watts each	...	24 watts
	Total power consumed	198 watts, say 200 watts

We next proceed to work out how many amperes of current will be flowing through the circuit when this amount of power is being consumed, and this is done by using Ohm's Law, according to which the amperage will be the total wattage divided by the voltage of the system. Thus, for 200 watts, 17 amperes will be required in the case of a 12-volt installation, or 34 amperes in the case of a 6-volt installation (both approximate). This

(Right) FIG. 9.27. *Marinized motor vehicle lamps, such as this Lucas handlamp with waterproof connexions, are available for small craft.* (Below) FIG. 9.28. *Lucas navigation lamps for stern, starboard, port, masthead or bow lights.*

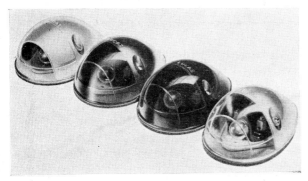

means that if a storage battery rated at 100 ampere-hours capacity is used, with a 12-volt system it will supply the total power load for about six hours $\left(\dfrac{100}{17} = 6\right)$ before becoming discharged. With a 6-volt system a battery of the same capacity would supply all the equipment for about three hours $\left(\dfrac{100}{34} = 3\right)$. Because there are losses of power in nearly all circuits these figures must be reduced by about 10 per cent, however.

From the foregoing it will be seen that if total power is likely to be required for longer periods, or if some margin of power is to be kept available for future electrical fitments, a battery of larger capacity will be necessary. The capacity required to suit individual cases can readily be worked out. It is true that the battery may only rarely have to supply power for all the equipment for any length of time, but it is best to plan the installation on this basis.

The next step is to decide whether to install a one-wire or two-wire electrical system. With a one-wire system one wire is used as the "live" line, while the metal of the engine or other parts of the boat are used as the return or "earth" line. (If more than one metal component is used for earthing there must be good electrical contact between the pieces.) With a two-wire system, separate leads are used for the positive and negative lines.

In a craft in which the lighting and other electrical equipment is grouped together around the control panel and close at hand in a cabin, the two-wire system can be recommended. Its advantage is that it allows the use of the

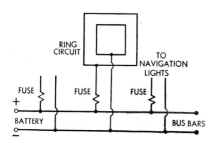

FIG. 9.29. *Simple three-fuse electrical circuit for lighting, etc. Two-wire installation allows the use of the ring circuit system.*

ring system of wiring (Fig. 9.29) whereby all lamps will give full brilliance. Where lamps are connected into one long length of twin wiring the last light in the line is sometimes quite dim owing to voltage drop along the circuit.

If the layout of the craft does not allow this type of installation a single wire can be used. One lead is then run from the switchboard to the fittings while the other side of the circuit is earthed. To provide a good earth in a fairly long wooden or plastic craft, a length of heavy bare copper wire can be routed through the accommodation and securely terminated at one end to the engine block. This earth line is not needed in metal-hulled craft, where the hull itself can be used for earthing, provided the connexions are made to bare metal. First-class electrical connexions and terminations are absolutely essential with any kind of single-wire installation.

Current can be lost through poor cable insulation, while the use of the correct size of cable for the power to be carried is essential. A suitable size

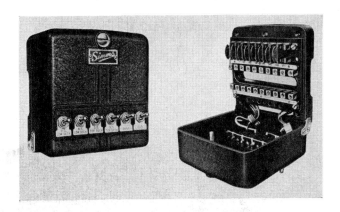

FIG. 9.30. *Automobile electrical fittings, such as this Simms switchboard for a double-decker bus, often make excellent installations in small craft.*

wire for cabin lighting wiring is 1/.044 in. For the main supply cable from the battery to the switchboard and fuse box use 7/.029 in. wire. P.V.C.-covered cable is excellent for all wiring, and all-insulated or plastic switches and fittings are recommended as they resist corrosion.

Incidentally, excellent installations in small craft can be carried out with the materials designed for use in motor cars and buses (Fig. 9.30). For a very limited installation, such as one or two lamps only, the supply line can be taken from the ammeter terminal while the return line should be earthed.

Auxiliary Generator. The problem of supplying a craft with a considerable amount of electrical power without depleting the engine supply can be overcome by installing a second generator, driven from the engine. What is needed is a machine preferably of the same type as that already fitted to the engine, which can be driven by pulleys and belting from either the forward end of the crankshaft or from a special pulley which can be attached to the propeller shaft. Installation is usually straightforward, but there may be some difficulty in getting the generator to operate at the required speed, especially if it is to be driven from the propeller shaft.

If the generator already on the engine turns at 1,400 r.p.m., for example, the auxiliary should revolve at the same speed. This is arranged by fitting pulleys of a suitable size, and the following formula can be used to calculate the pulley diameter:

$$D_2 = \frac{D_1 \times S_1}{S_2}$$

where D_1 is diameter of driving pulley, D_2 is diameter of driven pulley, S_1 is speed of driven pulley, S_2 is speed of driving pulley.

For example, if the speed of the generator is 1,400 r.p.m., the diameter of the pulley used to drive it is 6 in., and the speed of the engine shaft is 1,000 r.p.m., then:

$$\text{Dia. of driven pulley} = \frac{1,400 \times 6}{1,000} = \frac{84}{10} = 8\cdot4 \text{ or about } 8\tfrac{1}{2} \text{ in.}$$

FIG. 9.31. *Typical of self-contained marine generators, this 300-watt 24-volt Stuart installation would supply power for about eighteen lamps.*

The auxiliary generator should be mounted close to its driving pulley so that the shortest practicable belt can be used. Its output leads are connected via a voltage regulator to the auxiliary battery, and both the generator and the regulator must be well earthed, preferably to the engine.

Self-contained generating sets (Fig. 9.31) are usually installed in larger craft. An air-cooled engine is very suitable for driving the generator in such installations. The engine, with its generator directly coupled, can be mounted athwartships above the main engine if space is limited. The auxiliary batteries should be at waist level if possible, to facilitate maintenance.

CHAPTER 10

Outboard and Jet Engines

THE majority of outboard engines are of the two-stroke type, the working principle of which is outlined in Chapter 1. There may be one cylinder, two cylinders opposed or two cylinders in parallel. One important difference as compared with the normal inboard engine is that the outboard unit is horizontal, with the flywheel and ignition system mounted on top. Another feature is that there may be a small valve built into the crankcase to control the admission of fuel-air mixture into the engine (see Fig. 10.1). The fuel system is usually extremely simple. The electrical circuit differs from that used with inboard units, a self-contained magneto ignition system being fitted within the flywheel on top of the engine, similar to that used on many light motor cycles, scooters and motor-assisted bicycles.

Despite its comparatively small size and light weight the modern outboard engine is a rugged piece of equipment, designed to be both rain and spray proof. It has the same number of moving parts as a vertical engine— or fewer in some designs—and requires similar periodic maintenance. A representative selection of outboard engines, some of which are sectioned to show constructional details, are illustrated in Figs. 10.3, 10.4, 10.7, 10.8 and 10.10. Outboards today range from modest units of about 2½ b.h.p. to powerful engines developing 40 b.h.p. and more.

The action of the very simple carburettor is shown in Fig. 10.1. Fuel leaves the tank and flows into the float chamber until shut off by the rising float. The suction of the engine causes the fuel to enter the petrol passage which contains the jet for atomising the liquid petrol. The atomised petrol

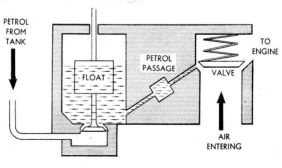

FIG. 10.1. *Arrangement of a typical carburettor for outboard engines. The valve to the engine is opened by suction from the piston as it rises, and closed by crankcase compression on the down stroke.*

FIG. 10.2. *Lockheed Avery Safelinc self-sealing coupling separated to show the positive-lock bayonet fastening. Used in conjunction with flexible hose, this coupling allows speedy disconnection of the outboard engine from a remote fuel tank when it is required to remove either unit from the craft.*

sprays into an incoming air stream and the petrol-air mixture enters the cylinder under the control of a spring-loaded valve.

When the suction of the engine is large (i.e., when the piston is rising), the valve opens and fuel mixture enters the crankcase. On the piston's downward stroke this mixture is partly compressed until the piston passes the by-pass passage, and when this is uncovered it allows the charge to enter the cylinder. When the piston is descending the valve is closed by the compression of the mixture trapped inside the crankcase. The valve is fitted with a very "soft" spring.

Some outboards use inboard petrol tanks. With these, part of the compressed fuel mixture in the crankcase may be piped through a non-return valve back to the fuel tank. The resultant pressure forces fuel from the tank into the carburettor. The tank, of course, is fitted with an air-tight filling cap which also incorporates a relief valve to prevent excessive pressure building up inside. Such fuel systems must be hand-primed to get the engine started. A quick and efficient coupling for separate fuel tanks is shown in Fig. 10.2.

The outboard engine magneto has primary and secondary coils which are similar in construction though not in appearance to those used with inboard engine coil-ignition systems. The magnet is attached to the flywheel and revolves with it, and a contact breaker and condenser are included. The circuit of a flywheel magneto is shown in Fig 10.5: this is for an engine with two opposed cylinders firing simultaneously. On two-cylinder engines with alternate firing there are two coils, two sets of contact breaker points, and two condensers. Four-cylinder engines have two plug leads from each coil. Secondary windings are connected to the plugs and the primary to the contact breaker points.

Transmission of the power developed is through a vertical shaft and bevel gears, one of the gear shafts being connected to the propeller (Figs. 10.3, 10.4). Some of the larger engines are also fitted with a clutch and

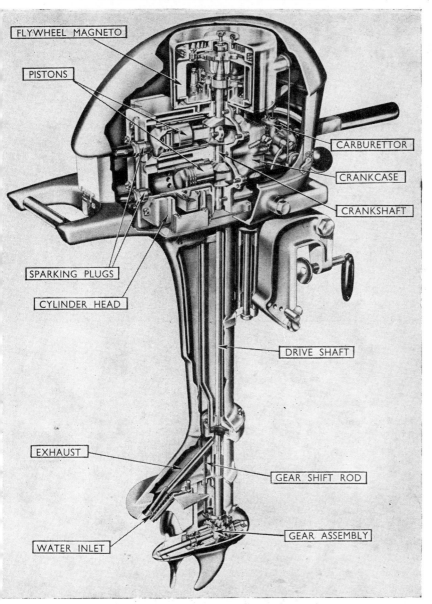

FLYWHEEL MAGNETO

PISTONS

CARBURETTOR

CRANKCASE

CRANKSHAFT

SPARKING PLUGS

CYLINDER HEAD

DRIVE SHAFT

EXHAUST

GEAR SHIFT ROD

WATER INLET

GEAR ASSEMBLY

FIG. 10.3. *Constructional details of the J. & F. Pool Medina twin-cylinder two-stroke outboard, which produces $7\frac{1}{2}$ b.h.p. at 4,250 r.p.m. This engine has forward and reverse gears, $3\frac{1}{4}$ gallon remote fuel tank with fuel delivery to carburettor by diaphragm lift pump, recoil starter and provision for fitting remote controls. With its Fibreglass cowling, the Medina unit weighs 59 lb.*

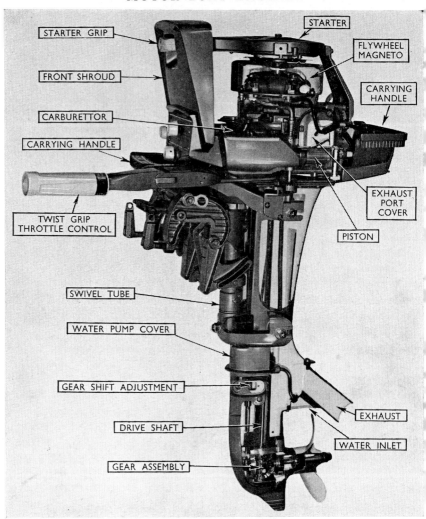

STARTER GRIP

STARTER

FLYWHEEL MAGNETO

FRONT SHROUD

CARRYING HANDLE

CARBURETTOR

CARRYING HANDLE

EXHAUST PORT COVER

TWIST GRIP THROTTLE CONTROL

PISTON

SWIVEL TUBE

WATER PUMP COVER

GEAR SHIFT ADJUSTMENT

EXHAUST

DRIVE SHAFT

WATER INLET

GEAR ASSEMBLY

FIG. 10.4. *A Perkins twin-cylinder two-stroke outboard engine shown part-sectioned and with its protective cowling removed. This unit, producing 6 b.h.p. at 4,500 r.p.m., is one of a range of basically similar engines which includes the 40 b.h.p. model shown in Fig. 10.9. It features alternate firing, automatic rewind starter, flywheel magneto, underwater exhaust, pressurised water cooling, and forward and reverse gears. The gear change and throttle are interconnected as a precaution against attempting to change unless the motor is idling. Fuel is delivered to the carburettor from the 2¾ gallon remote fuel tank by a vacuum-operated lift pump. This unit is available with short or long shaft to suit the craft's stern transom height, and its weight with cowl is approximately 50 lb.*

156

FIG. 10.5. *Circuit of a flywheel magneto for an engine having two cylinders firing together. Only one contact breaker, one coil, and one condenser are used. An alternate firing engine would require two contact breakers, etc. (compare Fig. 10.9 on page 160).*

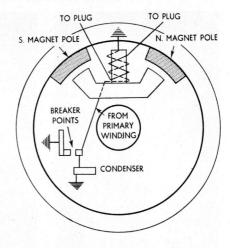

reverse gears. The smaller ones usually have no clutch, and reverse drive is obtained by turning the engine round completely on its mounting. A remote control system, such as the Teleflex (Fig. 10.6) can be added.

Most of the older engines, and also the cheaper current models, use pull-rope starting. A rope is wound around a pulley mounted on top of the flywheel, and a pull on the rope when the ignition is switched on causes the flywheel to revolve and the engine to fire. Unless the engine is in first-class condition more than one pull on the rope may be necessary.

Many modern units are fitted with automatic rewind or recoil starters. The principle is similar to the hand type but there is a coil spring built into the pulley and this causes the pulley to rewind the rope automatically each time it is pulled, thus saving trouble. On the larger models electric starting is common, working on the same principle as the starters used for inboard engines. The wiring diagram of such an engine is shown in Fig. 10.9.

Air cooling is used on some models, with an underwater exhaust to

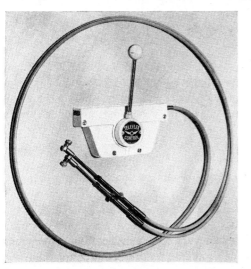

FIG. 10.6. *Teleflex single-lever remote control assembly incorporating gear and throttle attachments, and using stainless steel wires in plastic-lined conduits. Simple to install, the Teleflex is one of several remote control systems now available for outboard engines.*

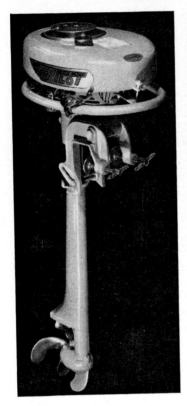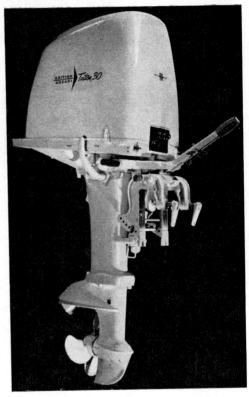

FIG. 10.7. *Two models from the well-known range of British Anzani outboard engines:* (left) *the single-cylinder Pilot which produces 2½ b.h.p. at 4,000 r.p.m. and has recoil starting;* (right) *the three-cylinder Triton, producing 30 b.h.p. at 4,800 r.p.m., and fitted with the Siba Dynastart incorporating a reversing feature.*

reduce noise, but most outboard engines are water-cooled. Either an underwater pump is fitted, which forces water up the transmission housing into the engine jacket, or water is forced into the system by the action of the propeller stream.

OUTBOARD ENGINE MAINTENANCE

Only a few precautions are necessary to ensure that an outboard engine runs satisfactorily. One of the chief causes of outboard trouble is dirty fuel and all petrol should therefore be strained before it enters the tank.

In the case of a two-stroke unit, the engine lubricating oil is poured into the petrol tank with the fuel. Whenever possible, the correct proportions of petrol and oil should be thoroughly mixed *before* being poured into the

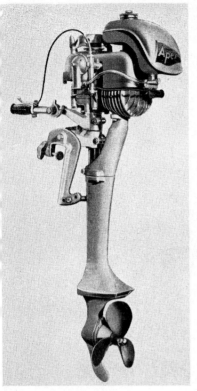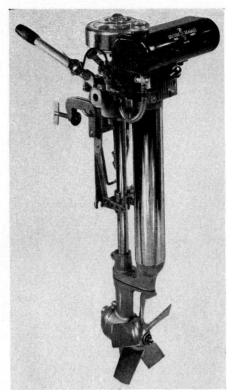

FIG. 10.8. *Two representative small British two-stroke outboard engines are* (left) *the Coventry Apex 85 de Luxe and* (right) *the British Seagull Century Plus. Both are single-cylinder air-cooled units weighing about 36 lb. Power production, respectively, is 3 b.h.p. at 3,500 r.p.m. and 3½-5 b.h.p. at 4,000 r.p.m.*

tank. If they are not properly mixed the engine will receive fuel mixture which is either too rich or too lean. What happens is that the oil sometimes settles at the bottom of the tank when it has not been well stirred up or given a good pre-start shaking. Then, when the engine starts, blue smoke is blown from the exhaust pipe and the engine fails to reach its top speed. Also, with too rich a mixture the spark plugs soon get dirty and misfiring commences.

Slowly, as the excess oil-to-petrol mixture is burned in the cylinders, the engine will gain more speed and the exhaust will clear up. But this can only last for a short time, because if the engine is not adequately lubricated there will be heavy wear on piston rings, pistons and cylinders, and the entire unit will heat up. Actual metal-to-metal contact may follow and the engine finally seize up. The correct amount of lubricating oil should be put into the fuel mixing can first, the petrol added, and the can well shaken before pouring the mixture into the tank.

Another cause of trouble is water in the petrol tank, due to condensation. When the tank is left partly filled, with its filler cap vent open, air will be drawn in as the engine cools. The moisture in the air then condenses on the

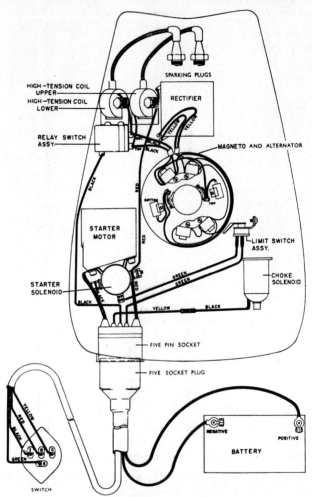

FIG. 10.9. *Wiring diagram for the electrics of a larger outboard engine—the twin-cylinder Perkins 35. Alternate firing of the cylinders requires the use of duplicate points, coils and condensers (compare Fig. 10.5). This engine features electric starting and provision for remote operation by solenoid relays for the starter and choke. Note the plug/socket connector for inboard battery and switch.*

inside wall of the tank. When too much water has collected in this way and mixed with the petrol, trouble will be caused through obstruction at the carburettor. The best preventative is to top up the petrol in the tank as soon as the craft has been stopped for the night, or else cover the tank vent until the engine is run again.

Apart from a clean supply of fuel, the outboard engine must have a strong spark and sufficient compression in the cylinders if it is to start easily and run without spluttering. The following methods will help to locate troubles in the minimum of time.

Failure to Start. If the engine will not start at all, first check each sparking plug. Clean and dry any plug which is dirty, greasy or wet, then place it on the cylinder top, in good contact with the metal, and pull the starter cord. If a strong white spark appears at the plug points it can be taken that the trouble is not in the ignition system.

If the spark is absent or very weak, the cause may lie in the magneto. Remove the magneto cover and clean and adjust the contact breaker points. If this does not result in an improved spark, the condenser may be faulty and should be replaced.

If the sparking plug testing shows that a strong spark is available, the fuel supply should then be checked. See that the vent in the filler cap is clear. Slacken back the petrol pipe at the carburettor and make sure fuel is reaching it. Clean any clogged or partly plugged lines with a length of flexible wire. Drain off the carburettor, if it is definitely receiving petrol, then replace all the connexions and try starting again. If the engine fires now, the cause of trouble may have been water in the petrol.

If the outboard is fitted with a separate tank, fuel may not be reaching the carburettor because of a stoppage in the engine-to-tank line. To check, hand-prime the engine. If the priming device is not functioning—it is sometimes merely a rubber bulb which can easily puncture—lift the petrol can or tank above the level of the engine so that fuel runs down the pipe to the engine. If the engine then starts, some way must be devised of holding the tank above the engine, such as resting it on an empty box placed on the stern seat.

If the priming bulb is holed it can be cut out of the line and a short length of plastic tubing inserted in its place. The tubing can be pushed over or into the petrol pipes and lightly tied in place or bound with adhesive tape. Leaks in the fuel tubing can be repaired in the same way.

Assuming that the engine is found to be getting adequate fuel, next examine the carburettor needle valve for damage. If this is bent it can prevent a sufficient amount of petrol passing into the air stream and the fuel mixture will be too lean to fire. Conversely, the engine can receive too much fuel; but this will have already been checked as it results in wet plugs.

If these tests show that the ignition and fuel systems are in good condition then the trouble must lie in the cylinders. The likeliest fault is lack of compression, and this can be checked as follows. Take out the sparking plug and place the thumb over the hole, then pull the starter cord. If compression is so low that air pressure on the thumb is barely perceptible, there is probably considerable wear on the piston rings, piston, cylinder, or all of these.

Giving the cylinder a good squirt of lubricating oil should improve the compression long enough to get the engine started. Once the engine does start give the fuel a double dose of oil to keep the rings well lubricated until overhaul can be carried out.

If an engine in good condition cannot be cranked and the starting cord is not jammed in any way, possible causes are: the bearings have been set up too tightly at the last overhaul; the crankshaft-to-propeller shaft is bent; the propeller gearing is broken and locking the transmission; the propeller drive shaft is bent. It may be possible to re-adjust over-tight bearings and avoid permanent damage, but bent or broken shafts and gears must always be replaced.

A rare but possible fault on a small engine is flooding of fuel to such an extent that it fills the cylinder and prevents the piston passing through top dead centre.

Faulty Running. Misfiring in an outboard engine may be due to dirty plugs or poor contact points. Sometimes a two-stroke engine will "four-stroke" as a result of these troubles—that is, it will fire every other revolution. Another cause of misfiring is too lean a fuel mixture.

When an engine runs hot, first check the cooling system for blockage in the water tube or inlet. Another cause of overheating is loosening of the flywheel magneto nuts, allowing the magneto to touch the flywheel. If this happens the engine will soon stop completely.

An extremely noisy engine is often a sign of propeller damage. Heavy vibration can usually be traced either to blade chipping or to slackness of the clamps securing the engine to the boat's transom. Very occasionally an outboard can literally squeal. This is a warning to stop at once, because it means there is insufficient oil in the fuel and the rings and piston are rubbing on the cylinder wall.

If the engine is to be left unused for a long period its fuel tank and fuel system should be completely drained, preferably by closing the fuel tank valve, letting the engine run until it stops, then removing and emptying the tank. If the petrol in the tank is allowed to stand for a long time exposed to the air it may form a kind of jelly which is highly effective for plugging thin tubing.

One of the most useful accessories for any outboard powered craft is a

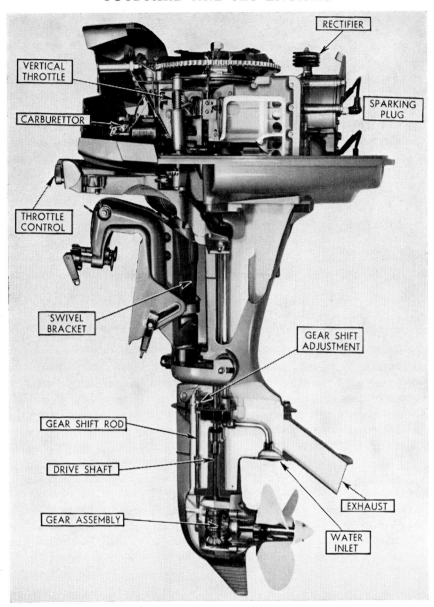

FIG. 10.10. *Perkins twin-cylinder two-stroke engine producing 40 b.h.p. at 4,500 r.p.m. Features are electric starting, forward and reverse gears, water cooling, 5½ gallon remote fuel tank, and a downward directed silencing system claimed to reduce engine noise by about 30 per cent. Extensive use of aluminium die-castings has kept the weight of this powerful outboard unit down to 130 lb.*

163

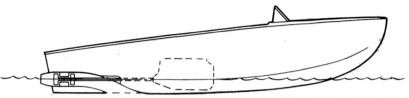

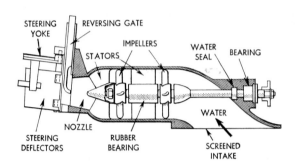

STEERING YOKE
REVERSING GATE
IMPELLERS
STATORS
WATER SEAL
BEARING
WATER
NOZZLE
STEERING DEFLECTORS
RUBBER BEARING
SCREENED INTAKE

(Above) FIG. 10.11. *Hull lay-out of the Dowty-Hamilton marine jet with a conventional inboard power unit (broken line).*

(Left) FIG. 10.12. *Working principle of the jet. A two-stage turbo-pump draws water through an intake and accelerates it for ejection at the stern.*

safety filling can with special spout. This allows the fuel to be well mixed and poured into the tank when afloat—a job which is otherwise almost impossible to complete when the boat is floating free without losing a great deal of petrol.

Running In. A new outboard engine must be run-in carefully, like any other engine, to allow its bearing surfaces to become properly bedded-in. Running-in instructions are given by the manufacturer and should be followed closely, but if these are not available the engine should not come to harm provided the following points are observed. For the first 25 hours

FIG. 10.13. *Steering mechanism and reversing gate fitted to the jet tail pipe on a Dowty Turbocraft. For steering, the flow of water is deflected to left or right; for reversing, the flow is deflected forward.*

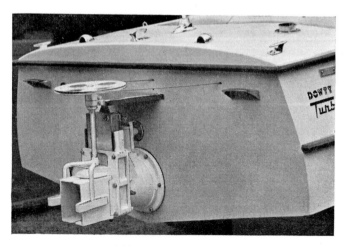

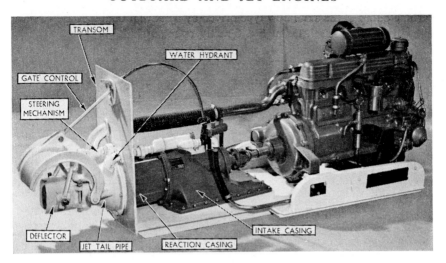

FIG. 10.14. *The complete Dowty jet installation with Ford Zephyr engine.*

running the engine must not be over-worked, so do not use more than half throttle and handle the controls gently. The maker usually recommends increasing the oil content of the petroil mixture, correct lubrication being vital during the running-in period. Increase the engine load gradually until, at the end of the first 25 hours, it is operating at full capacity. Then check the nuts and bolts, check all adjustments, and clean the fuel filter.

Laying Up. Many outboard engines are laid up after the summer season, when the following precautions should be taken: (1) If the engine has been running in salt or muddy water, run it for a short time in fresh water. (2) Drain the cooling system (if water-cooled), flush it out well with clean water and then drain very thoroughly. (3) Drain the fuel tank and every part of the fuel system to the last drop; clean fuel filters. (4) Remove the propeller, clean and lubricate the shaft, refit the propeller. (5) Remove the plug leads and plugs, and pour about a tablespoonful of engine oil into each cylinder. Replace the plugs and turn the engine over a few times so as to distribute the oil. (6) Drain the gearbox and refill with fresh oil. (7) Dry the engine thoroughly and coat all exposed metal parts with petroleum jelly or grease. (8) Finally, store upright in a dry place and protect by a covering of sacking.

JET ENGINES FOR SMALL CRAFT

Jet propulsion in various forms has gained increasing attention in the boat field during recent years. The advantage of a craft of the planing-hull type fitted with jet propulsion is that it can operate in very shallow water.

The usual marine jet system consists of a one-, two-, or three-stage turbine pump of the axial flow type driven by a conventional inboard engine, either petrol or diesel, through a directly coupled shaft. The pump draws raw water in at one end of its casing and discharges it with much greater velocity at the other end. The water is ejected from a nozzle attached to the boat's transom in the form of a powerful jet which strikes the surface of the water around the craft. The resulting reaction causes the hull to move.

One such system is the Dowty-Hamilton unit employed in the Dowty Turbocraft (Figs. 10.11 to 10.14). This is powered by a marinised 70 h.p. Ford Zephyr engine and employs a two-stage axial flow pump. Steering and reverse motion are obtained by deflecting the jet stream. For steering, a pair of pivoted box-like deflectors coupled together is used. For reversing, the flow of water must be deflected forward instead of aft. A steel screen is fitted over the water intake to prevent debris entering with the incoming water and so damaging the pump impeller.

The only maintenance work necessary for such an installation is an occasional check on the steering mechanism. When the efficiency of the unit begins to decline gradually the engine should first be checked in the ordinary way. If this is running with normal power the cause of the trouble is probably wear on the moving parts of the turbine pump. The jet unit should then be removed and returned to the manufacturer for overhaul. Stainless steel wear rings, as well as rings of other metals, are usually fitted to the pump casing immediately over the impeller tips where wear is heaviest. These can be removed and new rings pressed or screwed in.

If there is a sudden cessation of power, instead of a gradual decline, the cause is more likely to be partial blockage of the water intake screen under the hull. The obstruction may be due to pieces of sacking, old clothes, thick clumps of weed and so on, preventing normal inflow of water for the jet. The quickest remedy is to take the craft into water shallow enough to stand in and grope underneath the hull to remove the obstruction. If the screen is firmly choked, however, it will be necessary to haul the hull out of the water and make a proper inspection.

Somewhat similar jet systems have been developed by the Gill Propeller Co. Ltd. Here, however, the jet is discharged below the surface of the water. For going astern, a pivoted deflector is lowered, thus reversing the thrust.

Another jet system has been developed recently by Warren Marine Jets Ltd., in which there is no inboard engine driving a pump. In the Warren Hydrojet water is drawn in through an inlet and discharged through a suitable nozzle. There is a starter motor combined with a blower unit which delivers into a combustion chamber. In the combustion chamber, high-pressure gas derived from burning fuel is used to boost low-pressure air, which then passes through an expansion chamber to the ejector nozzle where it imparts considerable velocity to the water jet.

CHAPTER 11

Engine Cooling

In water-cooled engines the main duty of the water circulating through the engine jackets is to absorb and carry away the surplus heat generated by the burning of the fuel within the cylinders. Excess heat must be removed from the combustion spaces, exhaust and inlet valves, and in many cases from the exhaust manifold, too. If this surplus heat were not removed valves would soon overheat and burn, cylinder heads might crack, and piston rings would have a very short life. Worse still, the engine could seize up completely, as moving parts became hot enough to fuse together. Air-cooled engines, of course, are designed to operate without their components becoming hot enough to give rise to these problems.

Water cooling systems in marine craft may have the additional tasks of removing surplus heat from the lubricating oil and, in some installations, of cooling the shaft log (Fig. 11.1).

Several different types of cooling systems are to be found in motor boats, but in general they fall into three classes. These are :

1. Raw water or **direct cooling.** This is the most common system. "Raw" water is the water in which the craft is floating, either fresh or salt. It is sucked in from over the side, pumped through the engine jackets and other parts of the system then discharged overboard, as shown in Fig. 11.1.

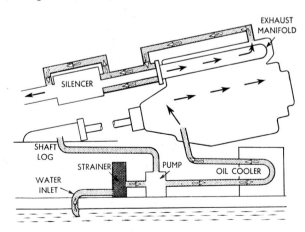

Fig. 11.1. *Passage of "raw" water through a direct cooling system. The coolant is led to the oil reservoir before circulating through the engine, and a separate supply is pumped to the shaft log, if water-cooled.*

167

2. Fresh water cooling, also called the closed system. In this, the water which passes through the cooling passages is taken from a mains supply on shore or is chemically treated to prevent scale formation. This "clean" water is pumped to a heat exchanger where it passes through tubes around which circulates raw water sucked in from over the side. This raw water

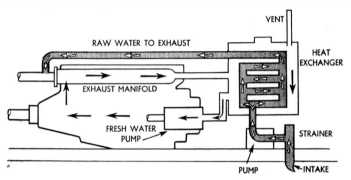

FIG. 11.2. *Passage of raw water and fresh water through a closed cooling system.*

absorbs the surplus heat and is then discharged overboard, while the fresh water is returned to the engine jackets to absorb more heat (Fig. 11.2). Two coolers of this type are shown in Figs. 11.3 and 11.4.

3. Keel cooling. In this system the hot engine water is passed through pipes attached to the outside of the hull or set into it (Fig. 11.5). Fresh water is supplied from a tank located above the highest point of the cooling circuit. It is pumped cold into the engine jackets, circulates round the exhaust manifold and then rises into the header tank. From here it is piped to the silencer jacket and then enters the exterior cooling pipes (sometimes called the external heat exchanger). The cooled water is then returned to the pump for recirculating. The complete system is shown in Fig. 11.6. The header tank can

FIG. 11.3. *Serck combined cooling unit for smaller high-speed diesel and oil engines. It comprises a header tank, with engine water heat exchanger and lubricating oil cooler which are raw-water cooled.*

168

FIG. 11.4. *Serck tubular heat exchanger. Heat is removed from the fresh water circulating through the assembly of tubes by raw water passing round them.*

be fitted with a thermostat to maintain the temperature of the water within required limits. Keel cooling is not recommended for craft operating in shallow waters, as the cooling tubes are liable to damage through grounding.

The essential parts of the first two systems are a sea valve in the hull below the water level to admit the water (Fig. 11.7), a water circulating pump, and a hull fitting to discharge the water overboard. In many modern craft, however, the water is discharged through the forward end of the cylinder block into the after end of a water jacket surrounding the exhaust manifold. It is then discharged over the side or into the exhaust pipe. (In the latter case it helps to quieten the exhaust as well as to cool the piping.)

A strainer must be fitted at the hull inlet to prevent the entrance of weeds, bits of wood and other rubbish. In the case of metal-hulled craft there is often a sea chest or box riveted or welded to the hull, and containing the strainer plate. Wooden hulls are seldom fitted with a sea chest. If the hull inlet strainer becomes choked, as may happen when the craft is working in shallow, muddy water, the cooling system will quickly overheat.

When there is a valve between the raw water inlet and the pump it must be kept fully open while the engine is running. In craft operating in cold waters some operators partly close the valve to reduce the flow of water

FIG. 11.5. *Thornycroft keel cooler (or external heat exchanger).*

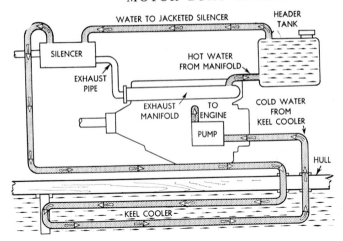

FIG. 11.6. *Circulation of the coolant through a keel cooling system. The external heat exchanger pipes may be fitted on the hull (Fig. 11.5) or set into it.*

and so maintain higher cooling water temperatures, but this should only be done as an emergency measure. When the incoming water is too cold for satisfactory engine operation its temperature should be controlled by a thermostatic valve, which will divert part of the incoming water overboard while allowing some of the warm water to be recirculated instead of discharged. Alternatively, a hand-controlled valve can be fitted in the inlet pipe *after* the pump. This will prevent the pump losing its suction and causing serious overheating trouble. The valve is closed in to restrict the flow of water, until the correct discharge temperature is reached (Fig. 11.8).

Cooling water must always enter the water jackets at the lowest point possible. It is then pumped upwards towards the top of the engine. This

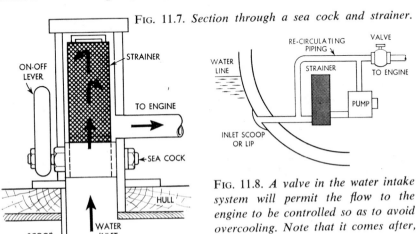

FIG. 11.7. *Section through a sea cock and strainer.*

FIG. 11.8. *A valve in the water intake system will permit the flow to the engine to be controlled so as to avoid overcooling. Note that it comes after, not before, the pump.*

keeps the engine filled with water at all times and prevents the formation of air pockets. Leaving the engine block, the water enters the cylinder heads where it cools the exhaust and inlet valves. Cooling of the inlet valves is not as important as that of the exhaust valves, because they operate in a stream of comparatively cool incoming air whereas the exhaust valves operate in the path of the red-hot combustion gases. From the cylinder heads the coolant passes to the manifold jackets.

Engine efficiency depends to a great extent on temperature—the higher the temperature, up to a point, the greater the efficiency. If temperatures are allowed to rise too high, however, salt and other deposits will build up in the jackets and impair the cooling. When salt water is the coolant the discharge temperature should be kept below 125 deg. F. to prevent salt scale formation. If fresh water is used, the desirable maximum temperature is about 140 to 150 deg. F. Should the water temperature be allowed to reach 180 deg. F., steam will form, causing pockets in the circulation system which develop into "hot spots" and lead to overheating troubles often difficult to trace.

Pumps used in the cooling circuits should have a capacity at least 20 per cent in excess of the amount that will be demanded by the engine when running at top speed. If an engine needs 10 gallons of water per minute, for example, the minimum pump capacity should be 12 gallons per minute. A widely used pump is shown dismantled in Fig. 11.9.

When a closed system is installed it is possible to regulate the temperature accurately. This can be done manually or with a thermostat. The amount of fresh water in the system must be checked daily and when necessary the expansion tank level must be topped up (Fig. 11.10).

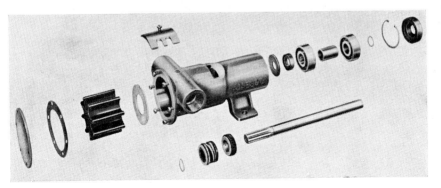

FIG. 11.9. *Jabsco 1-inch heavy-duty water pump dismantled to show the parts. Pumping action is obtained by means of a flexible neoprene impeller revolving against a ramp which bends the blades to create a vacuum at the inlet and a compression at the outlet. The pump is self-priming and self-lubricating.*

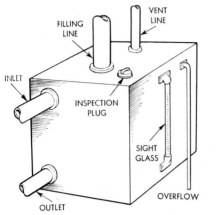

(Left) FIG. 11.10. *A well-designed expansion tank for a fresh water cooling system should feature an inspection plug, sight glass, overflow, vent line and filling line. The outlet should be raised above the tank bottom so that rust can settle out.*

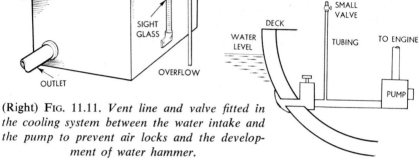

(Right) FIG. 11.11. *Vent line and valve fitted in the cooling system between the water intake and the pump to prevent air locks and the development of water hammer.*

Venting of the cooling system is important as it prevents the formation of air locks or water hammer. One excellent method is shown in Fig. 11.11. All that is necessary is to fit a $\frac{3}{16}$ in. or $\frac{1}{4}$ in. dia. copper pipe into the inlet pipe by welding, brazing or tapping; it must enter on the inboard side of the seacock strainer, and the open end must be taken well above water level. The open end is fitted with a special vent valve or is closed in by squeezing it until the aperture is about $\frac{1}{8}$ in. wide. Some manufacturers recommend the installation of a vent line on every craft.

SCALE REMOVAL

Cylinder block passages, especially in engines using sea water as a coolant, must be cleaned at regular intervals. All cooling water, whether from tap, stream, pond, river or sea, contains some impurities in the form of dissolved salts but sea water particularly so. When water containing these salts hits the hot engine surfaces the salts can be precipitated and left adhering to the metal in the form of a hard scale (Fig. 11.12).

Two kinds of scale may be found inside a cylinder block: the hard, white or grey, limey scale caused by precipitation of salts, and the flaky, reddish, metallic scale which is actually rust.

The presence of scale is difficult to detect other than by visual inspection. A reasonable idea of the general condition of a cooling system can be obtained by inspecting the inside of the water jackets in the immediate vicinity of the inlet and outlet water piping. Complete prevention of scale

FIG. 11.12. *An example of typical scaling in the passages of a diesel cylinder head caused by the precipitation of impurities from the cooling water.*

is virtually impossible when sea water is used. The control of scale in a closed cooling system is much easier, as the fresh water can be treated with chemicals to inhibit its formation.

Scale removal from the cooling passages must be done chemically since cleaning by means of scrapers and brushes is obviously impracticable. In closed systems it is possible to circulate the cleaning fluid through the engine without difficulty, but in the open type it is necessary to block off all connexions, fill the system with a cleaning fluid and allow it to stand for a while.

There are a number of excellent proprietary cleaners on the market which can be recommended for the job. The manufacturer's instructions should be followed in each case. Where no proprietary chemicals are available, the following method will work quite well with a closed system.

1. Drain the engine of all water. This may not be too easy as the bottom of the engine is normally close to the bottom of the hull and only shallow tins can be used to catch the coolant when the drain plugs are removed. If the water is allowed to run into the bilges one should first make sure that it will be possible to drain these. A hand bilge pump can be used, or a pump can be connected into the drain plug and the water pumped directly overboard.

2. Refill the engine to one half of its total fluid capacity, including the oil cooler, heat exchanger, etc. The capacity can be ascertained from the engine maker's handbook.

3. Boil an equivalent amount of water in a container and add ordinary washing soda until no more will dissolve. This is a strong solution and can be made up in batches if the system holds a considerable quantity.

4. Add the soda solution to the water in the cooling system. Do this with great care because the solution can burn the paintwork and injure the eyes and skin.

5. Run the engine at average speed for 5 to 10 hours.

6. Drain and flush out with clean water, and finally refill the system with fresh water.

When sea-water cooled jackets have to be scoured a much stronger cleaning fluid is needed to soften the salt deposits. Muriatic acid can be used in the proportion of one part acid to two parts water by volume. Great care is needed when making up this solution as it is highly corrosive and will cause injury to the skin, burn holes in clothing and attack paint work. The mixture is prepared in an acid-proof container such as a large stone crock or glass carboy and the acid must be carefully added to the water, *not* the water to the acid.

The solution is poured into the engine as shown in Fig. 11.13. The exhaust manifold can be cleaned separately. All parts other than the actual

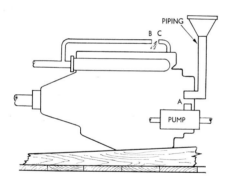

Fig. 11.13. *Scale removal in an open cooling system. The pump is disconnected from the water jacket inlet (A) and replaced by a length of piping terminating with a funnel. The exhaust line is disconnected at B and the cleaning fluid poured in via the funnel until it begins to run out at C, showing the system is full.*

engine block (water pump, discharge piping, etc.) should be blanked off as the acid solution will damage copper, brass, zinc and solder. When poured into the engine the solution will bubble furiously. After the bubbling has subsided the solution can be drained off. Its disposal must also be a matter of some care because it will still be quite active.

To prevent rust forming in a closed system a pint of paraffin can be added to the cooling water or, better still, a suitable rust inhibitor used.

WATER LEAKAGE; ELECTROLYSIS

If there is an external leak in the engine cooling system this will soon be detected when wiping down with the cleaning rag. An internal leak cannot be seen, but may make itself known by diluting the lubricating oil in the sump. The presence of water in the oil will be indicated by a cloudiness of the oil on the dipstick.

A small proportion of water in the oil is almost inevitable because water which is present in the combustion gases in the form of vapour can blow by worn rings into the crankcase, where it will condense and drip into the sump. But any indications of unusually large quantities should cause the operator to suspect that the cooling water is finding its way into the crankcase.

If the presence of water is due to fracturing of the cylinder metal or of the underside of the cylinder heads it can easily be located. One symptom of this is when an engine cannot be cranked to start although it was running perfectly when last shut down. What happens is that the small cracks allow the water to drip into the combustion spaces where, if the rings are in good condition, it collects until it fills the entire combustion space. When the engine is again started the piston cannot pass through top dead centre as the water cannot be displaced, unless the piston is rising on the exhaust stroke. This condition is called a hydraulic lock.

Cracks in the engine block can be repaired by experts but often it is cheaper to buy a secondhand replacement or fit a new unit.

Damage to the engine water passages can sometimes occur because of electrolytic action. This arises from the fact that different metals have different electrochemical characteristics, and when two metals of widely different electrical potentials are placed near each other in salt water, an action similar to that of a battery is set up between them. The result is that one of the metals becomes rapidly corroded.

This may happen between, say, a copper sea-water pipe and a cast-iron crankcase, if there is a gasket separating them: the iron will become corroded or eaten away inside. In such a case the two metals should be bridged together with copper strip or a "pigtail" type of flexible metal strap, ensuring good electrical connexion at both joints.

The external piping used for a sea-water cooling system should for preference be made of seamless copper, nickel or brass tubing. If this is too expensive, however, malleable iron pipes serve quite well.

CHAPTER 12

Clutches; Gears; Governors; Remote Controls

I<small>N</small> most inboard marine engine installations the power produced by the engine is transmitted to the propeller shaft through a clutch and reduction gearing. Reversing gear is also fitted to allow the craft to go astern, and the usual gear control has three positions: Ahead, Neutral (when no engine power is transmitted to the propeller), and Astern.

The clutch is a device which enables the engine to run without delivering any power to the propeller shaft. If this were not possible the propeller drag on the "dead" engine together with the effort needed to turn the gears and shafting would make it extremely difficult to start any but the smaller engines.

Reduction gears, as the term implies, are used to reduce the speed of the propeller shaft relative to the engine; they are necessary in craft where the engine runs at fairly high speeds, for if the propeller revolved at the same speed as the engine crankshaft there would be a serious loss of propulsive power. In modern engines the clutch, reduction gears and reversing gear are built into one unit which forms an integral part of the main engine.

CLUTCHES

The clutches used in marine transmissions vary in design from the simplest type of "dog" clutch to the more complicated automotive types, while there are special units designed exclusively for marine applications.

Dog Clutch. This is usually formed of two metal disks or flanges (Fig. 12.1). One of these disks has two or more dogs, i.e. rectangular projections, and the hub of this section often has a square-shaped opening which fits on to a squared section of the driving shaft. The clutch control is usually connected by a forked lever to the flange hub, and when it is operated the flange carrying the dogs slides along the squared part of the shaft. The dogs engage in matching slots cut into a mating flange attached to the gearbox shaft, which causes the two flanges to rotate together.

This type of clutch is robust and reliable, and rarely gives much trouble, though after a good deal of service burrs may be formed on the dogs. These

176

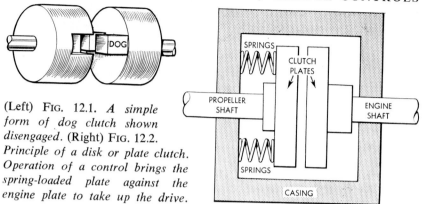

(Left) FIG. 12.1. *A simple form of dog clutch shown disengaged.* (Right) FIG. 12.2. *Principle of a disk or plate clutch. Operation of a control brings the spring-loaded plate against the engine plate to take up the drive.*

burrs, which can make it difficult to engage and disengage the clutch, may be removed by means of a fine file or stone. Another trouble is misalignment, which makes clutching and declutching a hard, noisy operation. This can be cured by re-aligning the engine to the gearbox. Wear on the bearings supporting the clutch shafts can cause the flanges to move out of line, again making it difficult to engage or disengage the clutch, and causing considerable grinding noise if the dogs are forced home.

Disk Clutch. This type is used extensively in marine installations. Similar in principle to the type of clutch found on most modern motor cars, the disk clutch consists of a driving plate (or "friction disk"). This plate has a central hub provided with splines or grooves. The splines match long external teeth machined into the clutch shaft, the arrangement permitting the disk to slide along the shaft and to rotate it.

When the clutch is in the engaged position, a set of strong springs forces the disk into tight contact with the outer face of the engine's flywheel (Fig. 12.3). The drive from the engine crankshaft will then be transmitted through the flywheel to the disk, then by way of the splined hub on the disk to the clutch shaft, and so to the gearbox. When the clutch control is moved to the disengaged position, the disk is pulled away from the flywheel (sliding along the clutch shaft) and therefore no longer receives the engine's drive. This allows the ahead or astern gears to be engaged without fear of damage to the gear teeth, or the gear lever can be moved to the neutral position. For going ahead or astern, after the gear lever is moved to the required position the clutch plate automatically re-engages with the flywheel to take up the drive.

In nearly all craft a single control lever is used to operate both the clutch and the gears, and separate clutch operation, as in the case of motor cars, is therefore unnecessary. Some craft are fitted with multiplate clutches

(Fig. 12.4). These employ a series of plates instead of a single disk, but the principle of operation is the same as described above. In some types of disk clutch, the driving plate is coupled to the engine's flywheel through a toothed ring, as shown in Figs. 12.3 and 12.4.

The main trouble likely to develop with a disk-type clutch is clutch slip, when the disk is not making full contact with the flywheel face. This causes loss of power and rapid wear of the clutch linings. It is more often found with high-speed than low-speed engines. Clutch slip is not always easy to recognise, but among its symptoms are: a gradual decrease in the amount of time and effort needed to engage or disengage the clutch; overheating of the clutch housing, sometimes severe enough to cause a distinct smell of burning; and a slowly developing reduction in speed.

While clutch slip will result in increased wear on the clutch, the normal amount of wear experienced by the mechanism over a lengthy operating period can itself lead to slipping. Clutch plates are made of steel or a suitable alloy, and are faced with some kind of material to provide frictional contact. These friction materials include the softer metals, cork, asbestos and fibre compositions. When the thickness of the facings is reduced by wear there will be less pressure between the surfaces and this allows the clutch to slip. Some clutches can be adjusted to take up this wear, detailed adjusting procedure being given in individual manufacturer's handbooks. Clutches fitted with springs slip when the springs weaken or break. The only remedy is to replace the springs.

Other causes of clutch slip are as follows. When an engine is repeatedly overloaded the amount of power that the clutch surfaces have to transmit

FIG. 12.3. *Rockford gear-tooth drive single-plate clutch as fitted to marine gearboxes. The outer ring is bolted to the engine flywheel, and its teeth engaged with the peripheral teeth of the face plate. The drive is transmitted through the clutch when pressure is applied to friction facings as in an ordinary disk clutch. The principle can be seen in the sectional view of the twin-plate clutch in Fig. 12.4.*

is greatly increased, and eventually a point is reached when the clutch commences to slip. The only way to prevent this is not to overload the engine. Clutches in which the friction facings are dirty will also slip; they should be cleaned with paraffin oil. Yet another cause is engaging the clutch at too high an engine speed. Engines must not be raced when the clutch is engaged, as the practice only leads to unnecessary wear.

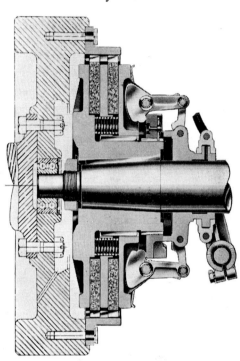

FIG. 12.4. *Construction of the Rockford gear-tooth drive 14-inch twin-plate clutch. This type of clutch is employed on the larger marine diesel installations where a heavy-duty transmission unit is required.*

When a clutch cannot be made to engage it is often described as being "frozen". The trouble can usually be traced to one of the following: control rods and gearing loose, excessive control bearing clearances due to careless adjustment, loose set screws and nuts on bell-cranks or other linkages.

Another trouble that may occur with disk clutches is a tendency to engage with a sudden grab or snatch, despite careful operation. Damaged or loose clutch facings, or broken clutch springs, are possible causes.

Cone Clutches are used in some craft. A cone clutch is one in which the driving and driven members are truncated cones in shape. The externally coned member is usually the driving unit, and moves axially in and out of the internally coned unit to engage and disengage the drive. When a cone clutch slips it can be adjusted by moving the driven cone along its threaded shaft closer to the driving cone. This is done by slackening back the locking

179

nuts, moving the cone forward about one-eighth of a turn, and locking it again. If this does not cure the trouble the adjustment must be repeated until all slip is eliminated.

REDUCTION AND REVERSE GEARS

As already mentioned, on most modern small craft the gearbox forms an integral part of the engine assembly and this facilitates the alignment of the sterngear. In those cases where the gearbox is separate from the engine the propeller flange on the gearbox shaft must first be aligned to the propeller shaft and then the engine is aligned to the forward gearbox flange, as described in Chapter 2.

There are many types of reduction gear in use but they generally operate on the same basic principles. It may be mentioned that although their normal purpose is to reduce the engine shaft speed so as to operate a slower and more efficient propeller, in some high-speed craft step-up gears are used instead of reduction gears in order to increase the propeller speed.

Band brakes are used in some gearboxes as part of the reversing mechanism and these are often referred to as "band clutches". The ahead clutches in these gearboxes can be of either the plate or the cone type. With this arrangement, slip in the astern position can be caused due to insufficient pressure being exerted by the reverse band on its drum. The band is usually fibre-lined, with brass rivets holding the lining to the metal band. The band can be easily adjusted to bring greater pressure to bear on the drum and reduce the slip. However, when the lining is badly worn it may have to be replaced in order to eliminate the slip. When riveting the new lining to the band, care must be taken to countersink the holding rivets.

Fig. 12.5. *Thornycroft Type B oil-operated marine reverse gear. Oil pumped through the mainshaft is channelled through one or other of three oil ports within the clutch assembly to force the driving member into engagement with the ahead or the astern driven member, or hold it free in the neutral position. Drive ratios from 1:1 to 3·5:1 are available.*

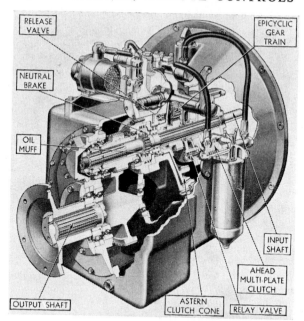

FIG. 12.6. Oil-operated gearbox employing multiplate clutches for the ahead drive and neutral, and a cone clutch operating a planetary gear for the astern drive, made by Self-Changing Gears Ltd. Control is by a rotary selector valve. A range of helical geared units is available for direct attachment when reduction gearing is required.

RELEASE VALVE

EPICYCLIC GEAR TRAIN

NEUTRAL BRAKE

OIL MUFF

INPUT SHAFT

AHEAD MULTI-PLATE CLUTCH

OUTPUT SHAFT

ASTERN CLUTCH CONE

RELAY VALVE

In some gear units, such as the Thornycroft, shown in Fig. 12.5, two clutch members are used to give ahead and astern drives. Other types use bevel gears to go astern, and there is an oil-operated reverse gear (Fig. 12.6) which has a multiplate clutch for ahead movement and a cone clutch and planetary train of gears for going astern. Yet another type (Fig. 12.7) uses cone clutches for both ahead and astern.

A few specialised craft use gearboxes having more than one ahead gear, the operator changing "up" or "down" as in driving a car.

While on the subject of gearboxes, V-drives may be conveniently mentioned, an example of which is shown in Fig. 12.8. These permit the engine to be mounted in the stern, giving more cabin space and easier

FIG. 12.7. Coventry Victor oil-operated gearbox suitable for smaller installations. The unit gives forward and reverse drives engaged by cone clutches, and offers standard drive ratios of 1:1, 2:1 or 3:1. Control is effected by means of a hand-operated valve.

181

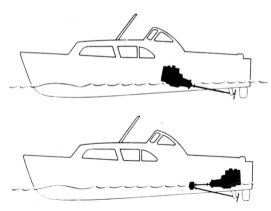

FIG. 12.8. *The ENV-Drive Type 1400 and its pair of spiral bevel gears. This unit is suitable for engines of 75 to 100 b.h.p., and is available in standard ratios of 1:1, 1·428:1 or 2:1. The drawings on the right show how the V-drive arrangement (lower picture) makes more cabin space available.*

accessibility for servicing. The drive is through a special narrow-angle gearbox, with or without speed reduction as required.

The servicing of gears is a simple matter. All gears must be checked annually for pitting of the teeth, which can arise because of corrosion, errors in alignment, or the use of dirty lubricating oil. The ordinary boat operator cannot, as a rule, effectively repair damaged gears. If the pitting has been caused by corrosion or abrasives in the oil the gear casing can be flushed out, thoroughly cleaned and new oil added. Gear teeth should not be stoned or filed as this will alter the tooth contour and increase rather than reduce the possibility of damage.

Occasionally there are complaints that the oil in the gearbox has begun to foam, even to the extent of bubbling up through the gear-case vent or filler cap. The common cause of this is overfilling the gearbox. The proper oil level in the box should never be exceeded. In a few cases it has been found that foaming has been due to the use of an unsuitable oil.

Gears wear in time, and the amount of wear can be determined by measuring the distance between the teeth with a feeler gauge. If excessive it will lead to a condition called gear growl, a low hum which becomes louder when the load is heavy but may almost vanish when the engine is idling. There is no solution to this trouble except installing a new gearbox. Gears that "growl" will often wear for years without causing any more trouble than the noise, however.

When there is trouble with the clutch or gears and consequent difficulty in going astern, all approaches to landings, locks, etc., must be made with extreme caution. As a further aid in stopping quickly a bucket can be kept standing by on the stern, lashed to a cleat, ready to be thrown overboard should the engine fail to respond at once to the controls. This will take the way off the craft very quickly, acting as a kedge anchor.

SPEED GOVERNORS

Governors fitted to the smaller marine craft may be described as being of the "limiting speed" type as they control the idling speed and prevent the engine stalling, ensuring that the maximum engine speed is not exceeded, and at the same time give the operator complete control between these limits. There are three types: mechanical, hydraulic and pneumatic. The hydraulic type is not often used in small craft.

In a mechanical governor the centrifugal force produced by rotation of the flyweights or flyballs (Fig. 12.9) is transmitted by suitable linkage to the fuel pump or carburettor throttle controls. With most types, increasing the speed of the flyballs tends to reduce the flow of fuel. However, a further measure of control is provided by springs which oppose the centrifugal force and *increase* the fuel flow. The net result is that the faster the flyballs revolve the less fuel is delivered to the engine; conversely, the slower they turn the greater the amount of fuel supplied.

Hydraulic governors also use flyballs but in this case the fuel flow is controlled by a piston operating in an oil-filled cylinder (Fig. 12.10). As already mentioned, hydraulic governors are not so likely to be found on marine engines, but they are often used to maintain constant speeds on such equipment as auxiliary electrical plant.

The pneumatic governor, found on many small diesel engines, utilises the varying depression (or suction) in the engine's inlet manifold resulting from the passage of air through a restricted zone of venturi form in conjunction with a throttle valve.

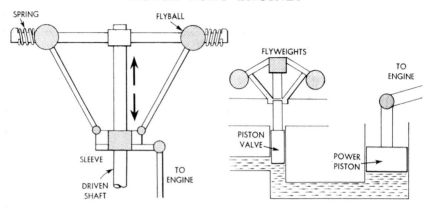

(Left) Fɪɢ. 12.9. *Principle of the mechanical speed governor.* (Right) Fɪɢ. 12.10. *Principle of the hydraulic governor. Both types of governor use flyweights, the basic difference being in the method of linkage to the engine.*

Fig. 12.11 shows the assembly of a typical mechanical governor for diesel engines. The governor consists of two wedge-shaped flyweights or balls pivoting on pins which are secured to the governor hub. The hub supports a sleeve, one end of which is in contact with the toes of the weights while the other end contains the fork running in a ball bearing. The crank lever, which pivots about the fulcrum pin, is located in the fork. A telescopic link connects the control rod to the top of the crank lever.

The two governor springs, main and secondary, are of the simple tension type and are connected to the lower crank lever and to the spring arm, which is fixed to the control lever cross shaft. The control lever is limited in its movement by stop screws which set the maximum and minimum speeds against a stop quadrant fixed on the control lever cross shaft. The rack stop on the front of the pump sets the maximum delivery to the pump. When required, a movable rack stop may be used to provide excess fuel for cold starting.

When the diesel fuel pump is required to operate at full load the control rod is moved to the "maximum delivery" position as follows. First the control lever is moved to a given speed position. This action loads the governor spring, causing the crank lever and the hub spindle to move forward against the toes of the weights and so bringing the weights inwards. In this position the centrifugal force of the weights is less than the spring load and at a speed below that selected by the control lever, so the control lever remains in the maximum fuel position.

Should the engine load decrease with the control lever in the same position, the engine speed will rise above the selected speed. This will cause the governor weights to move outwards and move the control rod from the maximum fuel position towards the minimum fuel position. Any movement of the control lever will increase or decrease the load of the governor springs and vary the engine speed.

Any load exerted on the governor springs will thus tend to move the control rod, through the crank lever, into the maximum fuel position. The engine speed at which the governor will operate is determined by the load exerted through the springs against the governor weights. The idling and maximum speed positions are obtained by adjusting the idling-speed stop screw and maximum-speed screw respectively against the control quadrant.

Maintenance of this type of governor is very simple. It normally needs only to be serviced every week by adding clean engine lubricating oil through the combined filler and breather. Overfilling should be avoided as this can cause sluggish operation.

A pneumatic governor for diesels is shown in Figs. 12.12 to 12.14. This consists of a venturi flow control unit (located between the induction pipe on the engine and the air filter) and a diaphragm mounted directly on the fuel injection pump. The body of the venturi unit is flanged at one end so that it can be secured to the induction pipe, and spigoted at the other end to accommodate the air filter. The diameter of the throat varies with the type and size of engine.

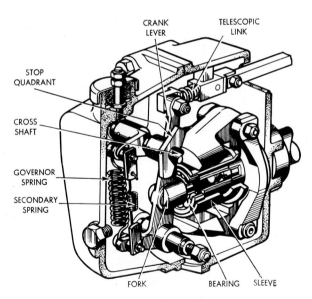

FIG. 12.11. *Typical of mechanical governors fitted to diesel fuel injector pumps is the Simms Type GMV All-Speed, shown here in part section.*

185

FIG. 12.12. Governor unit of the C.A.V. pneumatic governor, dismantled to show the diaphragm and the main diaphragm spring.

Air flow through the throat of the venturi is regulated by a butterfly valve 3 which is mounted on a spindle carried in bushes pressed into the venturi body. The control lever 1 is secured to the butterfly valve spindle and is connected by suitable control linkage to the speed control lever. Maximum and idling speed stops provide means of adjusting the movement of the butterfly valve.

A small auxiliary venturi situated within the main venturi may be secured to or cast integrally with the body of the venturi unit. Projecting into the

FIG. 12.13. Lay-out of a C.A.V. pneumatic governor fitted to a diesel injection pump. Details of the governor and venturi units are shown in Figs. 12.12 and 12.14.

1. Venturi valve control lever
2. Venturi throat
3. Venturi butterfly valve
4. Vacuum pipe union
5. Vacuum pipe
6. Diaphragm housing union.
7. Diaphragm housing
8. Main housing
9. Diaphragm
10. Main diaphragm spring
11. Stop lever
12. Oil cap
13. Control rod stop
14. Auxiliary idling spring
15. Auxiliary idling set screw
16. Auxiliary idling plunger

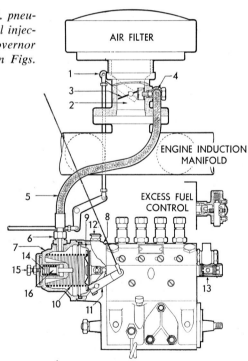

AIR FILTER

ENGINE INDUCTION MANIFOLD

EXCESS FUEL CONTROL

FIG. 12.14. *Venturi unit of the C.A.V. pneumatic governor, showing the butterfly valve and its control lever.*

auxiliary venturi at right angles to the air flow is a pilot tube connected with the diaphragm unit by the flexible tube 5.

The flexible leather diaphragm 9 is clamped between the governor housing 8 and diaphragm cover 7. It is connected to the control rod of the fuel injection pump and spring-loaded by the governor spring 10. Pressure exerted on the diaphragm by the spring tends to move the diaphragm and control rod towards the maximum fuel stop 13. Movement of the control rod is limited by adjustable stops, and idling speed is controlled by the set screw 15.

REMOTE CONTROLS

Although the governor controls the speed of an engine it does not start or stop it. To link up the engine with the bridge or control position in the craft, Bowden cables and flexible cables of similar type are extensively used for fuel, ignition control and so on. However, such cables are often too light for the operation of the ahead and reverse gear mechanism, and for gear operation other methods must be used.

Simple mechanical systems are popular, in which the operator moves a control lever

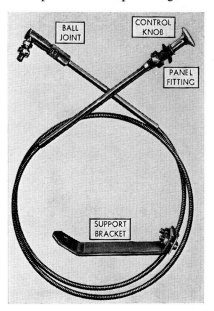

FIG. 12.15 *Amal flexible cable remote control suitable for operating the starter, choke or throttle on smaller craft. Cables up to about 12 ft. long can be used.*

187

which transmits the motion through links, bellcranks, rods and so on, to the engine. Solid rod can be used for this job but is rather expensive. Also, where the engine is located some distance from the control position a solid rod system becomes very heavy. As an alternative, lightweight tubing can be substituted, or even the conduit piping used in household electrical work. Yokes can be used to change direction of travel and fine adjustment made by using couplings secured with locknuts. Such tubing should be supported in well-greased brackets.

Professional equipment is also available from marine suppliers to make most mechanical hook-ups between the control position and the engine. Cable control systems are widely used. These may have flexible conduit (Fig. 12.15), suitable for use in smaller craft, or rigid conduit (Figs. 12.16 and 12.17).

Hydraulic remote control systems consist of a transmitter and receiver. They cannot be made up by the amateur, but professionally made equipment is easy to install and maintain. They have the advantage that the controls can be located at two points, if needed—one on the bridge and one in the after cockpit, for example. This dual control system is used by some

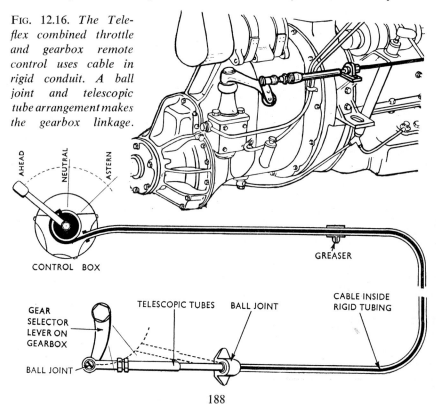

FIG. 12.16. *The Teleflex combined throttle and gearbox remote control uses cable in rigid conduit. A ball joint and telescopic tube arrangement makes the gearbox linkage.*

AHEAD   NEUTRAL   ASTERN

CONTROL BOX

GREASER

GEAR SELECTOR LEVER ON GEARBOX

BALL JOINT

TELESCOPIC TUBES   BALL JOINT

CABLE INSIDE RIGID TUBING

FIG. 12.17. *A complete Trianco installation showing a mechanical/electrical actuator with mechanical remote controls fitted to a Scripps V-8 petrol engine with Paragon reverse gear. Construction details of the individual transmitter and receiver units are shown on the right* (transmitter above). *Stainless steel is used for the cables.*

fishermen who, when hooked-on, wish to control the boat's speed from the stern.

The hydraulic system is fitted with a hand lever which moves a piston working in a cylinder in the transmitter end. The cylinder and the connecting pipe to the receiver are filled with a fluid which is incompressible. The movement of the transmitter piston is therefore transmitted through the fluid to the receiver, where it in turn operates a piston in another cylinder. This outward movement of the piston at the receiver end is used to operate the gear or engine controls. Provided the connecting pine and two terminal units are properly sealed against leakage of hydraulic fluid, practically nothing can go wrong in this system, and the controls respond exactly and instantly to movements of the hand levers.

CHAPTER 13

Sterngear; Rudders; Steering Gear

THE propeller shaft, its bearings and couplings, the stern tube and stern gland, thrust block, outboard bearings (if used) and propeller are collectively known as sterngear (Figs. 13.1 and 13.2). Correct design and installation is very important with all these parts, but maintenance is very simple and they normally give long service without trouble.

SHAFTS AND BEARINGS

Shafts must be strong enough to transmit the power developed by the engine to the propeller without any danger of bending or breaking. The best metals for their manufacture are high-tensile manganese bronze or stainless steel. Though these cost more than other metals which may be used, they give better service and are thus cheaper in the long run.

The end of the propeller shaft that enters the water is called the tail end. It must be taper ground to fine limits to mate with the taper of the propeller hub or boss: the usual Admiralty taper is 1 in 12. The taper section is followed by clean-cut threads to carry the propeller nut and the lock nut. Split pins, made of monel metal for preference, secure the nuts. If the engine is located some distance from the stern an intermediate shaft may have to be used to connect the tail shaft (as the propeller shaft is properly called) to the driving flange on the engine crankshaft.

As already mentioned, correct installation is most important, and the shaft diameters and details of propeller design most suitable for particular types of hull and engine speeds should always be obtained from the engine

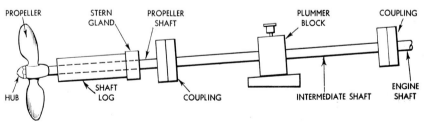

FIG. 13.1 *A typical sterngear arrangement including intermediate shafting.*

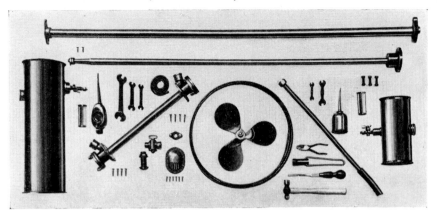

Fɪɢ. 13.2. *Sterngear, fuel tank, tools and other fittings supplied by the makers of the Brit E.10 petrol engine. Complete kits of this sort greatly simplify the work of installation.*

builder or hull designer. The correct dimensions cannot be guessed.

A shaft which has been delivered but is not to be fitted immediately should not be left lying about, nor should it be leaned against a wall as this will cause it to bend very slightly—enough to give trouble when lined up and in use. Shafts should be stored on a level surface and supported by blocks at intervals of 12 to 18 in. If delivered in a wooden box, which is the usual procedure, the shaft should not be removed until ready for installation.

Intermediate shafts must be supported on plummer blocks between the engine flange and the tail shaft flange. Plummer blocks are simple bearings lined with brass, gunmetal or babbitt metal. Swivel types are available but these are not generally suitable for marine work. Shafts of 1 in. diameter and exceeding 4 ft. 6 ft. in length should be supported by plummer blocks at a point midway between the engine flange and the tail shaft flange. Some builders recommend the use of two bearings for lengths over 5 ft. A two-inch shaft should be additionally supported if longer than 5 ft. 6 in., and a three-inch shaft if it exceeds 6 ft. 6 in.

Plummer blocks are screwed to the flooring or convenient frames and must be blocked up to match the shaft angle. This may seem a minor matter, but if the top half of a plummer bearing is pulled up and allowance is not made for the shaft slope, bearing damage will follow. Plummer blocks must be hand lubricated at intervals, or a better alternative is to fit them with grease cups or nipples which require only occasional attention.

The propeller shaft passes through the hull and enters the water via the shaft log and stern tube (Figs. 13.3 and 13.4). The stern tube can be described as an elongated bearing which allows the shaft to turn freely without

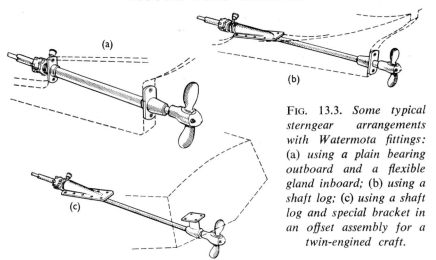

FIG. 13.3. *Some typical sterngear arrangements with Watermota fittings:* (a) *using a plain bearing outboard and a flexible gland inboard;* (b) *using a shaft log;* (c) *using a shaft log and special bracket in an offset assembly for a twin-engined craft.*

permitting more than a trace of water to enter the hull. A certain amount of water is allowed to trickle through in some types so as to help lubricate the shaft and the tube. Other stern tubes are supplied with water from the main coolant circulating pump in order to provide the necessary lubrication, this type of shaft log cooling being found particularly on high-speed craft.

Some stern tubes are packed with grease. With these, the cavity between the shaft and the stern tube walls must be grease filled before the boat is launched. The grease, of a special marine type, is forced into the stern tube from the inboard side, and when the outboard gland is slackened back it should slowly ooze out. The outboard gland should then be retightened (Fig. 13.5). To keep the tube full the grease cup should be given a few turns daily.

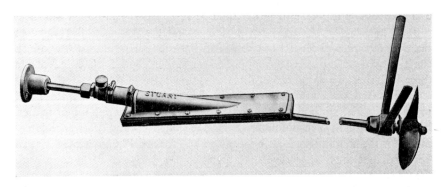

FIG. 13.4. *Stuart Turner adjustable shaft log which permits the inboard bearing to be swivelled 5 degrees up or down for alignment of engine and shaft. Also shown is a special "A" bracket which provides support for the outboard bearing.*

192

A gland is a short, round length of metal, generally of brass, which fits over the shaft and is either threaded or bolted on to the end of the stern tube. The gland may be filled with packing in the form of rings, called "turns", to stop an excessive amount of water leaking into the hull past the revolving shaft. These rings should be renewed annually. If compressed too tightly when they are fitted, the rings will burn and the gland metal overheat. Slackening back the gland so as to allow a slight flow of water to enter the

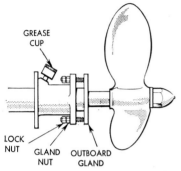

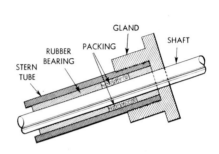

FIG. 13.5. *Stern tube gland fitting used with the Brit E.10 engine for petrol or vaporizing oil.*

FIG. 13.6. *Stern tube and shaft with rubber bearing. The packing is to prevent water entering the hull.*

hull will usually cure this trouble. Glands sometimes smoke when new packing is being run in, but a small amount of oil squirted on the shaft will help the new rings to seat quickly without overheating.

In many craft the shaft is supported by a rubber-lined outboard bearing (Fig. 13.6). If the shaft enters through the side of the vessel, as in wing or offset installations, both inboard and outboard logs can be used, as described in Chapter 2.

PROPELLERS

A propeller may be thought of as a rotary pump which pushes the boat along using a simple form of jet propulsion. It sucks water into the blades and then throws it out in a jet-like stream with great force. This jet of water, moving at a considerable speed, hits the surrounding mass of "solid" water and the reaction pushes the boat ahead. The shape of a propeller is that of a screw-thread section, and propellers are commonly known as screws.

Propellers are made in two-, three-, and four-bladed types. The two-bladed are found chiefly on outboard motors and high speed racing craft; three-bladed on pleasure craft with inboard engines; four-bladed mainly on the larger vessels.

The blades of the propellers used on sailing craft with auxiliary engines are made to "feather"; that is, when the engine is not in use the blades are turned so as to offer the least possible resistance to the water. Sometimes such blades can be folded so as to lie along the shaft, instead of being turned. Some types feather automatically while others have to be manually turned to the correct position and the shaft locked to prevent further movement.

An extension of the device of feathering is seen in the variable pitch propeller unit (Fig. 13.7) in which the blade angle can be completely reversed to provide astern motion.

If the propeller of a sailing craft is not locked when the hull is moving through the water under sail power only, the movement can cause the propeller to revolve. This causes the reduction gear also to revolve, and as in many cases the reduction gears do not receive lubricating oil unless the engine is running, heavy wear on the gears can soon take place. Engine damage has also been blamed on this movement. A so-called sailing clutch can be incorporated in the shaft to prevent such trouble. The clutch is operated when the vessel is under sail to disengage the engine and reduction gear, and the shaft is left free to turn without danger of mechanical trouble arising.

Propeller dimensions for small craft are always quoted in inches, the two measurements given being the diameter and the pitch. The diameter is always given first; for example, a propeller quoted as being 12 in. by 8 in. will have a diameter of 12 in. and a pitch of 8 in. The diameter is reckoned as double the distance from the centre of the hub to the blade tip, or the distance from one tip to the other in the case of a two-bladed propeller. The pitch is the distance the propeller should move the boat through the water when it has completed one revolution (Fig. 13.8).

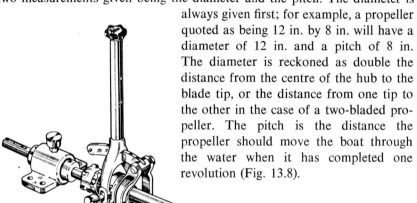

FIG. 13.7. *Astern motion in auxiliary yachts and other light craft may be conveniently obtained by the use of a variable pitch propeller such as the Watermota unit shown here complete with control gear.*

194

It must be noted that the vessel does not always move forward the distance indicated by the theoretical pitch of the propeller, some of the thrust being lost owing to cavitation, erosion of metal in the propeller blades, wind and water resistance, contrary currents, and so on. This loss, which can never be entirely eliminated, is called propeller slip and is quoted in the

Fɪɢ. 13.8. *Diameter and pitch of a two-bladed propeller. In the case of a three-bladed propeller, the diameter would be taken as twice the distance from the centre of the hub to the tip of a blade.*

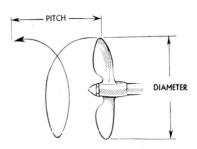

form of a percentage. As an example, if an engine turns a propeller with a 12-inch pitch 100 times, then theoretically the hull should move through the water a distance of 100 ft. If it moves only 80 ft. there is a loss of 20 per cent. This is the "slip".

In practice the slip is found by counting the number of revolutions turned by the shaft in one hour, multiplying by the pitch of the screw, and converting the answer into knots or land miles as required. The actual distance the craft has covered is arrived at by observation, and the difference between the two answers is expressed as a percentage.

Propeller blades which are damaged, even if only slightly, can set up severe vibration through the hull, while the loss of a complete blade may cause the shaft to fracture if the engine continues to run. Engines in the lower power ranges naturally use smaller propellers and any damage to their blades can greatly reduce their speed and efficiency. For instance, if one blade of a small two-bladed unit is only half an inch shorter than the other the loss in propelling power can be as much as 15 per cent.

Small craft with engines in the 3 h.p. to 8 h.p. range normally spend a great deal more time alongside than larger craft, and many operate continually in dirty, muddy water. To get the best from the boat under these conditions only the highest quality propellers should be used, as their power is so limited that a loss of propulsion efficiency as low as 10 per cent can cause a very noticeable falling-off in speed.

Propellers are made right-handed for engines turning clockwise and left-handed for those turning anti-clockwise. Twin-screw craft have propellers turning away from each other. To determine whether a propeller is right- or left-handed, place the palm of the hand on the rear or face of the blade. (It is the *rear* of the blade as seen from behind the boat that is called the face.)

If the curve fits the right palm it is a right-handed one. If it fits the left palm the propeller is left-handed.

Like the rest of the sterngear, propellers are designed to operate within specific speed ranges and with particular hull forms. When a propeller is ordered, therefore, the supplier should be given the following data: type of craft (motor boat, cruiser, sailing craft, motor sailer); the service in which it will be used (passenger, cruising, fishing, towing, etc.); its area of operation (sea, river, etc.); hull displacement, length at waterline and overall, beam and draft, and whether the boat has "fine" or "bluff" lines; whether it is a single or twin screw; ratio of the reduction gear; position of propeller (centre or wing); maximum permissible propeller diameter; expected speed; make and type of engine; horsepower; and, where possible, a hull diagram.

Ample space between the propeller tips and the hull is essential, and one rule used by designers is that this distance must not be less than one-sixth of the propeller diameter. A much greater margin is preferred where possible. Furthermore, if the best performance is to be obtained from the propeller the water must flow to it without hindrance. A better water flow can be obtained in some cases by cutting away the deadwood ahead of the blades and fairing the wood.

RUDDERS

Rudders must be designed to suit the hull and engine speed, and casual observation will show that a slow-moving scow has a huge rudder compared with the mere sliver of metal used on racing craft. Rudder shape and area is not arrived at by chance, and boat designers carefully calculate the surface area needed to make a boat respond to wheel and tiller movement.

For slow-moving craft such as auxiliary sailers the rudder is suspended from pintles from the sternpost. Twin-screw motor boats are fitted with two rudders, one behind each screw.

Virtually no maintenance is required for the rudder. One point which should be mentioned, however, is that the rudder will often be found to have

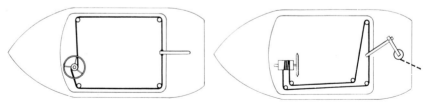

(Left) FIG. 13.9. *The simplest wheel steering system: the wire rope is carried from a drum under the steering wheel through sheaves at the corners of the cockpit, rope tension being maintained by turnbuckles.* (Right) FIG. 13.10. *A more complicated system which passes all the ropes to one side.*

FIG. 13.11. *Parts of a modern Teleflex steering gear suitable for outboard runabouts or for operating tiller steering on inboard-engined craft:* (left) *transom mounting with nylon ball joint to permit tilting of the engine;* (right) *quickrelease ball and socket connexion to the motor. The gear is cable-operated from a wheel mounted on the dashboard*

a small, unpainted zinc plate attached. This is to combat the action of electrolysis which was mentioned in Chapter 11. If the craft has a steel hull and a bronze propeller, the salt sea water will set up electrolytic action between the two different metals which results in corrosion of the steel. If zinc plates are fitted, however, these will be eaten away instead of the steel. The plates should be inspected at intervals and renewed at each overhaul. Galvanized bolts should be used to hold these plates.

STEERING GEAR

A wide variety of steering gear is available for use in small craft. The simplest kind is shown in Fig. 13.9, and variations can be made to suit a large number of hull shapes, such as that illustrated in Fig. 13.10. The Teleflex gear (Fig. 13.11) offers the convenience of a single control run by the use of flexible outer casing ("Bowden" fashion). It may be mentioned here that many boat designers recommend the use of a quadrant instead of a tiller when there is plenty of space aft.

Steering mechanisms which use chains and sprockets to give more positive control find favour in many craft. Some runabouts use cam and lever steering which is similar in every way to the automobile type.

CHAPTER 14

Pumps; Piping; Water Supply

A PART from such items as oil circulating pumps and fuel pumps, which have been dealt with under their appropriate headings, there are two types of pump likely to be found on a small marine engine installation. *Plunger pumps* are employed for bilge pumping and similar purposes, and are sometimes used to circulate cooling water. They are fitted with simple valves, often of the flap type. These need occasional replacement, and they have a tendency to stick in the open position if very dirty water is being pumped.

The other type of pump is the *centrifugal*, two examples of which are shown in Fig. 14.1, used particularly for pumping water through the engine cooling system. This is normally driven by the engine through a belt, chain or gear, or through a directly coupled shaft, and may include a clutch to allow the unit to be switched on and off without disconnexion from the engine. Or it may be a self-contained unit complete with electric motor drive, like the handy Stuart model illustrated. The pump casing contains a circular impeller rather like a paddle wheel, which rotates on a shaft. When the impeller is driven at sufficient speed, water is drawn in through the centre of the casing and discharged at high velocity through an opening in the outside of the casing.

Centrifugal Pump Maintenance. When the temperatures of the cooling water and lubricating oil both rise above normal the pump may be suspected of having insufficient discharge. If the trouble develops gradually it may be due to wear on the pump parts and cannot be corrected except by overhauling the unit and replacing the worn components. If such overheating develops suddenly, however, it will probably be due to an obstruction or damage in the suction system. The strainers should be cleaned and the suction piping checked for breakage. Occasionally the seat of the trouble will be found on the discharge side of the pump, when foreign matter of some kind has got into the water jackets or the tubes of the oil coolers or heat exchanger.

Another possible cause of insufficient discharge from a belt-driven pump is that its speed has been reduced through packing the shaft gland too tightly.

FIG. 14.1. *Centrifugal pumps for small craft. The portable Stuart Turner* (left) *comes complete with electric motor; the Jabsco* (right) *may be belt driven from the engine and incorporates a friction clutch.*

All centrifugal water pumps are fitted with a gland, an adjustable sealing device which prevents water entering through the shaft log. If the packing is squeezed too tightly it will bind against the shaft, causing overheating and reducing the speed of the pump by making the belt slip. In the case of a chain-driven, geared or shaft-driven pump, if the gland is packed too tightly the pump shaft will overheat and the metal will score. Glands must only be tightened to the point where a small amount of water is allowed to leak past—but the rate should not exceed half a dozen drops per minute.

If sand is drawn into the pump with the water it can cause pump shaft damage by being carried into the gland by the drips. There it is held against the shaft by the packing and results in scoring the shaft, necessitating replacement of the damaged parts.

Once in a while a pump shaft snaps. One possible cause of this is vibration, which can be due to a damaged impeller running off balance or to partial blockage of the casing. Bearings that are in poor condition can also lead to shaft failure.

Some centrifugal pumps are fitted with wear rings around the impeller, which take the main wear in running and are replaceable when worn. These depend upon the water to act as a lubricant between the rings and the impeller. If a pump is allowed to run dry the impeller will rub against the casing and both overheating and rapid wear will result.

Sometimes an impeller works loose on the shaft due to failure of the key. Keys and keyways should be examined for wear each time the pump is opened up. At the same time a check should be made for pitting of the shaft

199

and the bearings, as well as the impeller and casing. Such pitting is usually due to corrosion and can be accelerated by electrolytic action between parts made of different metals, as mentioned on page 175.

A self bailer is a U-shaped tube, one end of which picks up water from the bilges while the other is fastened to an extractor nozzle protruding through the hull below the waterline (Fig. 14.2). When the craft is moving ahead the passage of the extractor through the water creates a suction which draws water out of the bilge.

A strainer is fitted over the bilge end of the tube, and a non-return valve is incorporated to prevent any flooding back. Care must be taken to fit the

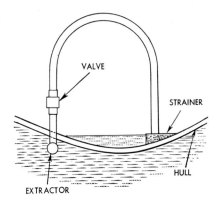

FIG. 14.2. *Self bailer positioned at the lowest possible point of the hull. The extractor must face away from the boat's line of travel and a non-return valve be fitted.*

extractor the right way round, with the scoop-shaped end facing away from the boat's direction of travel, or water will be forced up into the U-tube instead of being sucked out of it. The non-return valve should prevent this water flooding the bilge, but if the valve is leaking the water will enter the hull. It is therefore essential to keep it in good working order.

Piping carrying sea water should for preference be made of seamless copper-nickel, brass or copper. Where initial cost must be considered, the type of pipe fittings used for domestic plumbing will serve, but it will not wear or last as well. Between these extremes is a variety of different materials, the price of which is generally related to their durability. Plastic pipes have not yet been adopted for marine craft, but may well be soon: certain types have already given excellent service in town supply use. Excellent connexions for metal piping can be made with the standard fittings available from hardware stores.

Fresh water pipes should be of galvanized steel. Any connexions between the engine and piping which is rigidly secured to the hull should be made of flexible steel or rubber, to prevent damage from engine vibration. Leakage takes place at pipe connexions more often than elsewhere, and much of this trouble can often be obviated by giving the pipe better support against vibration.

The repair of damaged pipes is best left to skilled mechanics. The following notes will, however, serve as a guide to the different repair methods.

Welding is used on steel tubing and special welding fittings are available. The surface to be welded must be perfectly clean and free of rust and scale. A wire brush, file or emery cloth should be used to clean off the surfaces.

Brazing. Most copper, brass and copper-nickel tubing should be silver brazed, as brazed joints are far more resistant to vibration and high temperatures than soft-soldered joints. For brazing, the tube ends must be cut square with a hacksaw and only a proper brazing flux should be used: flux intended for soldering is not suitable. When the flux melts, the metal is at the correct temperature to commence brazing.

Soldering also is suitable for copper and brass piping. Cleanliness of the surface is more important in soldering than in welding or brazing; the outside of the tubing and the inside of the fitting should be cleaned with fine steel wool or glasspaper until no dark spots are left. The work parts must be hot enough for the solder to flow freely: a torch is better than a soldering iron. Only sufficient flux should be used to cover the working area, otherwise carbon will form from the burning flux and prevent a good bond between the surfaces.

Flared connexions. In making flared connexions the tubing should first be cut off square. A flaring tool of the proper size should be used; if this

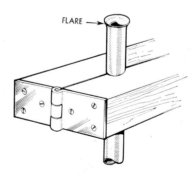

FLARE —

FIG. 14.3. *Tubes to be flared with a punch or drift can be held securely in the vice without damage by means of this simple clamp made from two pieces of wood hinged together and drilled out.*

is not available the tubing can be held as shown in Fig. 14.3, and the end tapped out with a punch or drift.

Pipe bending. When small-bore tubing has to be bent it should first be annealed. This is done by heating it to a dull red colour and then quenching in cold water. Then get a stack of washers and place them one on the other until the diameter of the tubing is obtained. Two wooden blocks are placed one each side of the washers and clamped in a vice. The end of the tube can then be hand bent. Alternatively, the tubing can be bound with soft wire (wire from packing cases is suitable) and then bent. This will prevent any distortion. Tubing of very small bore can be bent by inserting a length of soft copper wire which makes a fairly good fit inside. After bending the tube the wire is withdrawn. A length of solder, well greased, can also be used for this job.

MARINE TOILETS AND WATER TANKS

The marine toilet (Fig. 14.4) is something which is still not properly understood and has probably been responsible for more accommodation flooding than all the hurricanes of all times! In fact, it is quite a simple piece of equipment.

The main component is the pump (Fig. 14.5) which does a double duty. It draws in water from outside the hull and forces it into the bowl. Then it pumps the waste and water out through the discharge piping. With most types, both the inlet and outlet valves must be open when the pump is operated.

There is a disk or cup-shaped leather on each side of the pump plunger. When the pump lever is operated, the cup on top of the plunger draws the water in through a non-return valve on the downward stroke, so that the cylinder fills. On the upward stroke this water is forced through a second non-return valve into the bowl. On the same upward stroke the bottom cup causes the waste and water in the bowl to be drawn through a flap valve into the pump cylinder. On the next downward stroke this waste is forced through another flap valve into the discharge pipe and so overboard.

When the toilet is located below

FIG. 14.4. *Blake "Victory Superior" yacht toilet. Typical of modern practice, it replaces the simple flushing pump by a press-type flushing valve and booster pump.*

the waterline the waste passes through an inverted U-pipe, with the top of the bend above water and the discharge point below. A further rubber valve, shaped rather like a plumber's force-pump, is incorporated in the line to prevent the possibility of any back flow.

When a toilet does not work the first parts to come under suspicion should be the simple check valves admitting and discharging the water from the cylinder. If the inlet valve remains open water will just be sucked into the

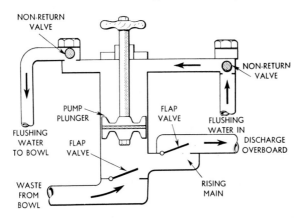

FIG. 14.5. *Principle of the marine sanitary pump.*

cylinder and then pumped back through the inlet pipe without reaching the bowl. If the non-return valve in the line leading the flushing water to the bowl sticks open or is worn, water cannot be drawn into the cylinder because of air leakage from the bowl. Bits of wood and weed can stop these valves operating, but they can easily be cleaned.

The leather cups on the pump plunger should be checked annually when the hull is overhauled. Remember that the toilet cannot be used when the boat is aground.

On the upper reaches of the River Thames and some other inland water-ways, only chemical toilets may be used in boats. These are convenient to use, but the manufacturer's instructions should always be followed closely.

Water Tanks. Fresh-water tanks can be located almost anywhere in the vessel. They should be made of rust-resisting metal, with openings sufficiently large to allow for cleaning out. These openings should have well-fitted watertight covers. Water tanks must be vented, like fuel tanks, and can be connected to a simple semi-rotary pump to supply water for domestic purposes.

CHAPTER 15

Monthly and Annual Inspections; Laying up

REGULAR maintenance inspections help to ensure trouble-free running. Small defects taken in time can save major derangements later. This chapter sets out the practical work which should be carried out each time the monthly maintenance checks and annual overhaul are undertaken, and when the craft is laid up for a period.

MONTHLY MAINTENANCE

Engine. Check for cracks in the crankcase and cylinder head and for indications of water, oil or compression leaks around studs, bolts, screws and gaskets. If a new gasket is installed tighten it three times: (1) when it is installed; (2) when the engine has reached its normal operating temperature; (3) after the engine has been operating for several hours. Examine the valve mechanism. Tappets, springs, rocker arms and other gear should all be secure and in good condition and the valve cover gasket must be renewed if leaky or damaged. The tappet clearances should be measured while the engine is hot or cold as specified, and adjusted if necessary to the values given in the maker's handbook. Lock nuts securing the valve adjustments must be tightened firmly.

See that the engine holding-down bolts are tight and that the side trays, if used, do not leak. Examine the condition of the inlet and exhaust manifolds and their gaskets, and check for leaks revealed by carbon streaks. Tighten all nuts and bolts securing these components.

Then, in the case of petrol engines, take out each sparking plug and check that its insulation is in good condition and that there is no compression leakage from the cylinder. Give particular attention to excessive carbon deposits on the plugs and to electrodes which have worn thin; worn plugs will need renewal. (These conditions may indicate the use of the wrong type of plug.) Clean all plug electrodes and adjust the gaps as necessary.

A test for compression should be made. With the engine warm, take out all sparking plugs and insert in a plug orifice a compression gauge or a simple Bourdon-type gauge reading up to at least 200 lb./sq. in. Turn the engine at cranking speed with the starter and record the reading on the gauge. Repeat this for each of the cylinders, then compare the figures with those specified in the engine handbook. If the compression is shown to be below normal, squirt engine oil into the cylinder and on to the piston head and rings, and repeat the pressure test. If the compression figure is now brought up to normal this indicates wear on the piston, rings, or cylinder, the oil having provided a temporary seal. If the compression remains low then the valves are most probably leaking and must be ground in.

With diesel engines, use a nozzle test stand if one is available to check the spray pattern and opening pressure of spray valves. Observe whether there is any after-dribble of oil, and whether the spray pattern is even and without "flags". Tighten all nozzle mountings and pipe connexions after refitting. Check the compression in each cylinder by attaching a pressure-gauge indicator reading up to at least 1,000 lb./sq. in. The readings should be checked against the figures specified in the maker's handbook. If compression is low, try the oil test mentioned above. If pressure is then found to build up, the cylinder, piston and rings need attention.

Fuel System. The carburettor on a petrol engine should be cleaned and a check made to ensure that none of the gaskets or unions are leaking. See that the throttle and choke valves open and close fully when the controls are operated. All exterior linkage to the carburettor must work freely without binding at any point. Drain and clean out the float chamber and check the jets for cleanliness.

The air cleaner on both petrol and diesel engines must be removed and cleaned in petrol or paraffin oil. See that its gaskets, seals and clamps are in good condition. In the case of oil-bath air cleaners, note the level of the oil and top-up if necessary. If the oil is dirty, drain and clean out the container, then refill with fresh oil.

Inspect the fuel tanks and ensure that these are in good condition and securely mounted. Examine the filler caps for worn washers and see that the vents are not plugged. Check all tubing and piping for correct support and tighten loose clips. Drain off accumulated water and dirt from the tank bottom. Remove fuel screens and all filters in the fuel system, including any at the carburettor, and clean these. Flush out the sediment bowls or sumps with paraffin oil before replacing.

Fuel pumps should be examined. If possible, attach a gauge to the fuel supply line and with the engine idling check that the delivery pressure from the pump is in accordance with the manufacturer's instructions.

In the case of diesel fuel injection pumps, tighten all mounting and assembly nuts and bolts. Check the level of oil in the pump sump and refill to the correct mark if necessary. Oil should be drained from the sump every two months and fresh oil put in.

Lubrication and Cooling Systems. Inspect all oil filters and oil coolers for leaks. Clean or change dirty filters. When a throw-away cartridge filter is to be replaced, first clean the filter case, otherwise grit will get carried into the engine.

Check the water in a closed cooling system. It should be drained and replaced by fresh water if dirty or discoloured. Examine any zinc electrodes that may be fitted and replace those that are corroded.

In the case of a fresh water expansion tank, drain the water if cleaning is necessary but first check whether it contains anti-freeze fluid. If so, catch the coolant in a clean container, flush out the empty system with a good flow of water, then replace the coolant after filtering it.

Pump and Accessory Drives. The pump drive, whether belt, gear or chain, must be properly adjusted. See that pulleys and sprockets are in good condition, correctly aligned and not excessively worn. Examine shafts for end play and loose bearings. Chains and belts should be checked for correct tension but should not be over-tightened. Drives on accessories should be similarly examined, and particular attention paid to drive belts. These should be replaced if they are frayed, soaked with oil or bottoming on the pulleys.

Electrical Components. Remove the cover band over the brush gear on the generator and inspect the commutator. Clean off any dirt with fine-grade sandpaper. The carbon brushes must be clean, work freely in their holders, make proper contact with the commutator under pressure from their springs, and not be excessively worn. An easy cleaning method is to place a strip of very fine sandpaper over a wooden block of the correct size and, with the engine just ticking over, carefully press the sandpaper against the commutator until it is clean. Wipe away all dust or blow it out with compressed air. Tighten all securing bolts and terminals on the generator.

The starter motor should first be checked by starting the engine and ensuring that the gear engages without delay. Clean any dirt off the starter gear that may be jamming it, but do not lubricate the gear. The commutator cover band should be removed and servicing of the commutator and brush gear carried out in the same way as for the generator.

The regulator cannot be serviced without proper instruments, and in any case is a specialist's job. However, its external connexions can be checked and tightened if necessary.

Ensure that the ignition coil is clean, dry and securely mounted, with its terminals tight but not over-tightened. Before opening up the distributor, wipe away all dirt and check the exterior connexions. Remove the moulded cap and inspect the rotor arm and plug contacts. There should be no cracks in the cap nor corrosion or looseness of terminals. Test the drive shaft for looseness by trying to shake it—excessive movement indicates that the shaft bearings need attention. Examine the contact breaker, and see that the gap when the points are fully open is correct, also that the points are clean and not badly worn. If the points are slightly pitted or burned, dress them with fine sandpaper. If badly burned, replace them by a new set and fit a new condenser at the same time.

The ignition timing (petrol engines) or pump timing (diesel engines) should be checked in accordance with the procedure given in the engine manufacturer's handbook.

Inspect the battery carefully; the casing, terminal posts and cell straps must be in good condition. Look for cracks or evidence of leaks in the casing and for corrosion of the metal parts. Check the electrolyte level. See that the vent cap openings are free. Measure the specific gravity with a hydrometer before topping-up with distilled water, and while the sample from each cell is in the hydrometer note the colour. If this is a reddish brown it can indicate that the battery is being overcharged through a regulator defect. Also, if a voltmeter is available, measure the voltage of each cell. If a cell's voltage is lower than the others by 0·1 volt or more, it is probably defective. Check that the battery compartment is well ventilated and all connecting cables and terminals are sound. Clean the top of the battery, if dirty, with a weak solution of ammonia or soda and lightly coat the terminals with petroleum jelly such as Vaseline, or a proprietary anti-corrosion jelly.

Gears, Pumps and Sterngear. Check the level of the oil in the gear case, where appropriate. Check for fractures in the casing if there appear to be oil leaks in the vicinity. (Gaskets may be the cause of the leakage.) Make certain that there is no stoppage in the bilge pump suction line and that the pump is operating. Tighten all pump mountings whether power driven or manually operated. Examine the propeller blades, particularly for any chips from the blade edges. Pay particular attention to shaft alignment, bearing mountings, glands, and the shaft log bearing. See that the rudder moves from the full port to the full starboard position without stiffness or binding. Such binding may be due to over-tightening of the rudder stock stuffing box.

ANNUAL OVERHAUL

The overhaul work—dismantling, examination, and re-erection—required at intervals by marine engines is very much the same for all types, both petrol and diesel. Detailed procedure is often given in the maker's instruction handbook or service manual, and only general guidance in the form of notes can be given in this section.

In the past it was usually found necessary to carry out a "top overhaul" on a marine engine about every three months. The attention included lifting the cylinder head, cleaning away accumulated carbon, checking and, if necessary, grinding-in the valves. With the increased reliability of the modern marine engine, top overhauls can generally be dispensed with nowadays, and it is only necessary to open up the cylinders when there is a loss of power due to leaky valves or some other internal trouble.

When an overhaul is to be made it is essential to follow a logical sequence in dismantling, examining and re-erecting the engine. A recommended method is to drain off all oil and water while the engine is hot, then disconnect all electrical leads and remove the battery, and then start dismantling the cylinder head.

Top Overhaul. Remove all the sparking plugs and examine these as described earlier (page 138). Loosen the cylinder head nuts and lift off the head. Check all studs for breakage, tapping them lightly with a hammer (not on the threads) to find out whether any are broken below the level of the cylinder block.

Remove the valves, using a valve spring compressor, and clean the guides with a strong bristle or soft wire brush. Valves should always be refitted in their original positions on the engine, and are often numbered to assist this. While the valves are dismantled they should be soaked in paraffin oil and then cleaned. If there is any burned carbon or gummy substance on the valve stem, rub it off with fine emery cloth soaked in paraffin or engine oil. This will take off the dirt without scratching the stem. Check the valves for burns on the contact area. A badly burned valve may be cleaned up by hand or by machine grinding. However, it is better to insert a new one as the metal under the burned area may have lost its ability to withstand heat and will soon give trouble through warping or burning.

The valve stems should be compared with new ones, and worn ones replaced if possible. If new ones are not immediately available, the worn valves can be refitted temporarily, but there may be some loss of power. The opportunity should be taken of checking the valve springs, too.

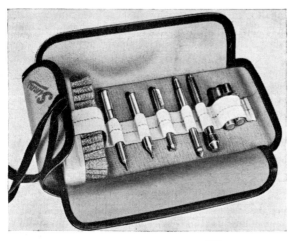

Fig. 15.1. *Simms cleaning kit for diesel fuel injector nozzles. The kit includes a set of special scrapers, prickers with a pin vice to hold them, and a wire brush.*

Check the valve seats. If the valve is burned the seat, too, may be damaged. A burned seat can be driven out with a drift of the correct size or with any suitable length of round bar. Care must be taken not to cant the seat otherwise it will jam. If it does jam the drift should be used to force it back into its original location before further efforts are made to extract it. Obstinate seats can be removed with a suitable puller. (It helps if the cylinder head is first heated in boiling water for about ten minutes.) New seats can be pulled or driven into place. Great care must be taken to avoid damage to the seat area and the seat recess must be perfectly clean and free from rust and dirt.

Diesel fuel injectors should be overhauled in accordance with the maker's recommendations, but they normally need little attention if the fuel has been adequately filtered. Dirty injector nozzles should not be neglected, as they result in fuel waste and a smoky exhaust. A kit designed for cleaning nozzles is shown in Fig. 15.1.

When the cylinder head is reassembled the valves can be tested for tightness by filling the passages with paraffin oil and watching for leakage on the underside. Place a piece of newspaper beneath the valve. This will absorb the smallest drop which may leak by. Leaky valves can be hand-ground until they seat perfectly in their ports.

In the case of air-cooled engines, the cooling fins must be examined for signs of cracks when the cylinder head is removed. Such cracks are quite rare, but if they do develop they can be stopped by drilling a hole at the spreading end of the crack, or the damaged area can sometimes be sawn or filed away. This may be a very difficult job, however.

Cylinders, Pistons, Crankshaft, etc. The cylinders should be checked for wear as described in Chapter 6.

Care is required when extracting and handling pistons and rings. Rings should be stacked in the order they occupy on the piston. This can best be done by hanging them on hooks in the order of their removal and numbered to coincide with the particular piston. Pistons, rings and grooves should be checked as described in Chapter 6. Note that the taper present in a piston should not be mistaken for wear on the metal. Pistons are deliberately tapered to offset uneven expansion, the top being smaller than the bottom.

The bearing metal or detachable bearings of the connecting rods should be inspected for any signs of roughness; this indicates either a badly bonded bearing or indifferent lubrication—more likely the latter. If the bearing metal is in fair condition, with no more than 10 per cent of the metal removed, it can still be used. A little scraping may be necessary to remove any high spots, but this work is best left to a skilled mechanic. Methods of checking the connecting rod bearing clearances are described in Chapter 6.

The crankshaft main bearing caps must be removed. Also, the crankshaft can be lifted if necessary, but this is not recommended as it entails the removal of the flywheel and shaft seals. There should be no need to take out the crankshaft, in any case, unless there is heavy wear and the crankshaft journals are to be reground.

The crank throws should be checked for size (see page 85), and any marks present can be removed by stoning. Clean all oil passages very thoroughly, using a flexible wire brush and then pulling through a stout rag (one which will not tear easily) soaked in paraffin oil. Check the pipes, borings or channels which deliver oil to the crankshaft from the oil pump, and see that these are clean. Camshafts must also be examined for wear, and particularly for chipping of the cams.

The tappets must be lifted out and cleaned after soaking well in paraffin oil. Make sure that the adjusting nuts and lock nuts are tight; the threads should not be worn to the extent that the nut can be spun with the fingers. Worn nuts or tappet threads make it difficult to maintain correct valve clearances and it is better to replace them when the engine is undergoing overhaul than to have recurring valve-timing trouble. The tappet guides rarely need attention.

Check the oil pump or pumps for wear. The simplest method of doing this is to shake the shaft in its bearings and measure the backlash of the gears. The oil pump is more important than many people seem to realise. If it does not function properly oil pressure will fall or the oil may cease to circulate altogether, and the engine will quickly be ruined. When there is any doubt about an oil pump's efficiency it is always better to replace with a new unit rather than risk the engine in this way. Wear on the pump can also be checked by dismantling and examining the interior of the pump casing. Look for marks at the ends which indicate that the shafts are moving very slightly in their bearings and the gears are touching the metal. This may seem to be a minor matter but it can lead to a dangerous condition, and it is best to replace a unit which has worn bearings by a complete pump.

Inspect the crankcase for fractures. Clean out any sludge in the crankcase, and the dipstick opening.

Timing gears should not be removed, but examined in place. Timing gear troubles are often caused through faulty lubrication. Sometimes teeth will be found to be chipped. If the teeth are badly broken the gear must be removed by the use of a suitable puller and replaced by another. The whole train may have to be replaced, in such circumstances. Before the new gears are used, however, the cause of the failure should be found : more often than not the trouble is insufficient oil.

Before re-assembling an engine each individual part must be thoroughly cleaned. If this is not done and dirt enters the lubrication system considerable wear on moving parts can result before the entrained particles are removed from the oil stream by the filters and strainers. All moving parts, including journals, rings, gudgeon pins and cylinder walls, should be well oiled before the engine is boxed up.

When the engine is started the lubrication system must be vented to rid it of air locks. With most installations this can be done by removing the filter casing plug. The water cooling system must also be vented if not fitted with a vent tube. This can be done either by filling the system from above —which entails removing the discharge pipe leading from the engine block to the exhaust manifold and filling it with the inlet valve closed—or by starting the engine with the exhaust manifold connexion loosened so as to bleed out the air.

Carburettor. After the carburettor has been cleaned by immersing it in paraffin oil or other cleaner, the following procedure can be followed:

1. Check the body for cracks. These are not a frequent trouble, but if they do occur they are more likely to develop at the engine flange than elsewhere.

2. Remove the float from its chamber and ensure that it is not leaking. If the float is of the hollow metal type it can be checked by immersing it in a glass jar containing petrol. Air will be observable bubbling from any leak, no matter how small.

3. Inspect the float needle, that is the tapered part which regulates the flow of petrol. If this is worn, as shown by a slight ridge, it is best to change it.

4. Remove the jets and blow through them the opposite way to that in which the fuel travels, so as to free any dirt. Check for damage to jets caused by dirt in the fuel, and fit new ones where necessary.

When the carburettor is refitted it must make a tight fit against the engine block, otherwise air will be sucked into the engine and result in too lean a mixture. A new gasket should therefore be fitted between the carburettor and engine block each time dismantling has taken place.

Electrical Equipment. The only overhaul work that the average operator can undertake on the starter motor, generator, contact breaker and other electrical units is that described earlier in this chapter. If such components develop troubles which require proper test equipment and knowledge of electrical work, they should be handed over to an electrical repair specialist. When the annual overhaul is carried out, however, the batteries should be cleaned and their electrolyte topped-up, as described earlier. It is good policy to charge them at the same time from a shore source of supply, and most garages will provide this form of service.

LAYING UP

When a small power craft is to be laid up for the winter months or left out of commission for a period, the following procedure should be adopted.

1. Unless the engine is being taken out of the boat for storing ashore,

drain off the fuel tanks and the engine. If possible, blow through the lines with compressed air, placing the air hose in the fuel tank and disconnecting the petrol or diesel oil supply line at the engine end.

2. Reconnect the lines.

3. Drain off the lubricating oil and, if the engine is due for an oil change, refill with new oil. Remove all the sparking plugs, pour about $\frac{1}{4}$ pint of lubricating oil into each cylinder and turn the engine over by hand or with the starter motor. This will lubricate all valves, rings and cylinder walls. Wrap the sparking plugs in oily rag and stow them in a metal box.

4. Drain all water from the cooling system. If possible blow through the system with compressed air. If a closed-circuit system is not to be drained, an anti-freeze mixture should be added in the proportion of one part to three parts of cooling water.

5. Drive a cloth-covered plug into the end of the exhaust pipe.

6. Insert old sparking plugs in the engine block. Seal the threads to the block with heavy grease to stop air entering.

7. Remove the starter motor and generator, wrap them in cloth and store in a dry place. Remove the battery, drain the electrolyte, and wash out each cell with water. The battery can then be stored without risk of sulphation. Alternatively, it can be left at a garage where it can be given an occasional charge to keep it in good condition. Batteries must not be allowed to stand in a discharged condition. If drained, they should be refilled with electrolyte and given an initial charge by someone with knowledge of proper charging practice.

8. Remove the lubricating oil filler cap and drive in a wooden plug covered with cloth to stop entrance of air.

9. Take off any air filters and tie stout cloth or canvas over the open end of the inlet manifold.

10. Make sure that the water pump is drained and the valve in the hull side tightly closed.

In the case of a diesel engine the following method may be used to protect the fuel system during the laid-up period.

1. Just before the engine is shut down for the last time warm up two quarts of lubricating oil (depending on engine size) to a temperature of about 180 deg. F. Stop the engine.

2. Disconnect the fuel line at the tank and place the end of this pipe in the hot oil. Start the engine and allow it to run until practically all the oil in the container has been sucked into the fuel system. Two quarts of oil will be sufficient for a large four-cylinder engine.

After the engine is shut down a small piece of jointing material can be taped over the fuel pump vent and the pump can be filled with a good brand of fresh lubricating oil.

Diesel fuel injectors can be covered with a thin layer of petroleum jelly or some other kind of heavy grease by way of protection.

The engine should be well wrapped in old blankets and covered with a waterproof tarpaulin, especially if the boat is to remain afloat.

SUBMERGED ENGINES

Sometimes it is necessary to salvage a craft which, through accident or negligence, has been under water for some time. What can be done to prevent further damage to the engine in these circumstances depends entirely upon how soon the work of overhaul can be started and, of course, the length of time that the engine has been submerged.

In the case of a diesel engine which has been under water for a few days or perhaps a week it is often possible to get it running in a matter of hours. First remove the spray nozzles and force the water out of the cylinders by hand cranking. Pour a few fluid ounces of lubricating oil into each cylinder and turn the engine over by hand for several revolutions so that the oil is spread over cylinders and rings.

Remove the fuel pump and drain it of water. Alternatively, take off the inspection plate; then, with the fuel pipes to the spray nozzles disconnected, work the plungers up and down with a screwdriver until all oil and water in the pipes is forced out. Replace the inspection plate and refill the pump sump with suitable lubricating oil.

Tanks, filters and fuel lines must next be drained and refilled with clean uncontaminated fuel. Take off all crankcase doors or the filler cap and pump out the water. If a hand pump or syringe is available, pump lubricating oil through the lubrication system.

If hand-started, the engine may now run. If it cannot be swung the spray nozzles should be loosened and then the engine cranked again. This will force out of the cylinders any surplus oil which might otherwise block the pistons and prevent them reaching the top of their stroke.

A petrol engine presents a more difficult problem as the electrical equipment must be dried out. This can be done by placing the components in a metal box heated with electric lamps. The temperature should be near but not higher than 180 deg. F. Above this temperature the water would boil inside the coil windings and other places, so causing new damage where there might not have been any before. The best plan is to have all the affected electrical equipment tested and serviced by a specialist before further use.

When time allows it is best to strip down an engine which has been submerged for more than a few days, and this invariably applies to an engine using electrical ignition. It is just as well to overhaul the whole installation generally at the same time.

CHAPTER 16

Byelaws and Accident Prevention

The importance of taking proper safety precautions in a small craft—particularly where petrol fuel is concerned—has already been stressed in this book. From time to time distressing accidents are reported where a boat blows up or bursts into flames. The risk of loss of life is obviously even greater in these circumstances than when similar accidents occur on land.

The Ship and Boat Builders' National Federation, concerned by such accidents, have issued recommendations for the prevention of accidents in pleasure craft with inboard engines, arising from fire, explosion and suffocation. These recommendations are confined to the *minimum* precautions deemed both reasonable and desirable with petrol-engined craft. The following extracts are reproduced by permission of the Federation.

A. PETROL ENGINE INSTALLATIONS

Tanks should be made of a suitable non-corrosive material of adequate thickness for the capacity of the tank and should be capable of withstanding 2 lb. per square inch pressure. Suitable baffles should be fitted in tanks, leaving not more than 3 cubic feet between baffles. In the case of metal tanks, all joints and seams should be brazed or welded, or rolled and soldered or riveted and soldered. A vent pipe to the outside of the boat should be incorporated in tanks of 10 gallons capacity and over; in tanks of less than 10 gallons capacity an adequate vent hole should be provided in the filler cap. The vent pipe should be of adequate size in relation to the bore of the filling pipe.

Tanks should be rigidly fixed on bearers and installed as low as possible and as far away as practicable from the engine. Where tanks have to be fitted in the engine room they should be suitably encased.

Petrol filler should be taken to deck so that any petrol overflowing will go over the side of the boat and not in the bilge. The filler pipe should be taken to the bottom of the tank, to effect a seal whilst filling, on any tank over 5 gallons capacity. Petrol-resisting rubber hose and good quality clips may be used to connect the deck fitting to the tank but joints must be tested to ensure that they are petrol-tight.

Piping, Fittings and Flanges. All fittings and flanges for unions should be brazed or welded or riveted and soldered. The petrol feed should be carried in softened copper pipes of suitable size so fixed as to minimise vibration, and with a flexible connexion to the engine. Petrol-resisting flexible tubing may be used provided the tank is electrically bonded to the engine. All unions and fittings should have metal-to-metal joints, or be brazed on to the pipe. Soft solder should not in any circumstances be used.

Petrol Pumps. Where an electrical pump or other suitable mechanical means be employed, petrol should be drawn through the top of the tank by means of a pipe running to the bottom of the tank.

Gravity Feed Systems. Gravity feed is not recommended, particularly where tanks exceed 2 gallons capacity. If gravity feed is employed, a tap must be fitted at the bottom of the tank. If the tank tap is not easily accessible, a second tap should be fitted in an accessible position as near to the tank as possible.

Flame traps should be fitted wherever possible to all except crankcase compression engines and a screened drip-tray fitted to all carburettors other than those of down-draught type.

An engine tray wider and longer than the engine should be fitted under each engine to catch any oil or petrol to prevent it from going into the bilge.

B. BUTANE GAS INSTALLATIONS

(This section is omitted as it is outside the scope of the present book.)

C. GENERAL CONSTRUCTIONAL RECOMMENDATIONS

Means of Escape. Where the normal exit from living accommodation leads over an enclosed engine space an alternative means of escape should be provided.

Fire Extinguishers. Sufficient fire extinguishers according to size of the boat, type of fuel and fuel capacity, should be carried and placed outside the compartments they are intended to serve. At least one dry powder (gas pressure) type or CO_2 or foam type hand extinguisher to be installed on every cabin yacht or mechanically-propelled boat. Dry powder extinguishers of the canister or pistol type are not recommended for marine use. Methyl bromide extinguishers should in no circumstances be used and C.T.C. and chlorobromomethane (C.B.) extinguishers should not be carried where danger exists of their being used in confined or badly ventilated spaces, because under certain conditions the fumes given off are liable to be dangerous.

Ventilation. Thorough ventilation of engine, fuel tank and bilge spaces is essential. In each such separate space there should be a minimum of two air trunks, one of these extending to the lower part of the space. As an alternative one or more extractor fans may be fitted, but these should be of explosion-proof type. All accommodation spaces to be provided with permanent ventilation of a type that cannot be closed.

Insulation. The exhaust pipes and silencer should be efficiently water-cooled or lagged.

Batteries. To be adequately secured and compartment well ventilated. No battery to be fitted under any petrol tank, cock or filter.

Electrical Wiring. The battery should be as near to the starter as is compatible with safe stowage arrangements. Adequately sized leads to be taken direct to the starter via the starting relay contacts. The relay should be mounted direct on the starter or adjacent to it.

Wiring with necessary fuses should be taken through proper junction boxes to the various point fittings and the wire cleated at intervals of not more than 12 in. and installed as high as possible. In no circumstances should wiring be carried under floors or in bilges.

Wiring to be preferably of the stranded cable type (not solid conductor), and it is recommended that P.V.C. covering, being impervious to petrol, oil and water, should be used.

Care should be taken to keep wiring from running near exhaust pipes or other forms of heat and clear of places where loose objects may knock against it.

Where the installation load is in excess of 15 amperes the main fuse should be capable of taking the full load and be further broken down by a fuse splitter immediately following it, so that each separate circuit is protected by its own fuse.

THAMES LAUNCH BYELAWS

Certain of the official bodies controlling our inland waterways have issued byelaws or other regulations designed to ensure the safety of boats using their waters, and of navigation generally. The Specification as to the Construction and Equipment of Motor Launches under the Thames Launch Byelaws, 1952, is of particular interest, and extracts from this Specification are reproduced below by permission of the Thames Conservancy.

Part I: INBOARD MOTORS

Carburettors. Carburettors (other than down-draught carburettors) which can be flooded or which might overflow must be so fitted as to allow any overflow to drain into a copper, brass or galvanised iron drip tray. Such drip tray must be spirit-tight and must have a top of copper or brass gauze of flame-resisting mesh sweated to the container all round. Such drip tray must also be of sufficient length to come under the air inlet as well as under the carburettor, unless there is a flame trap fitted, and, unless emptied by other approved means, must be readily removable for emptying. When a down-draught carburettor is fitted, or when the fuel is petrol mixed with oil, such drip tray need not be fitted. Wherever possible a flame trap must be fitted.

Fuel tanks. Fuel tanks must be constructed of copper, or an alloy of copper, or of steel efficiently galvanized after making up, or of other approved material. Seams to be properly lapped and sweated or riveted and such tanks must be installed in such a position that ready access can be had to all connexions. Drain cocks on tanks to be locked shut or blanked off below the cock. Fuel tanks should preferably be installed in separate compartments as far as possible from engines and heating appliances. Where it is necessary to fit a fuel tank close to any engine, the tank must be encased with metal plates lined with asbestos or other heat insulating material.

Filling of pipes. Where the filler pipe on the fuel tank is not connected to the deck filling hole the space between must be sealed off to prevent petrol getting into any other part of the launch when the tank is being filled.

Fuel pipes. All fuel pipes must be of seamless drawn soft copper or other approved tubing, and must be fitted with an approved form of joint, and in all cases so fitted that ready access can be had to them and to all connexions throughout their entire length. Where cone nipple connexions are used, the nipples must be either brazed or silver soldered or effectively pressed on. No soft soldered joints to be used. The main fuel pipe must be provided with suitable bends or coils for giving it the necessary elasticity. No glass filter bowl may be fitted in the vicinity of an engine, or an oily bilge, unless a steel baffle plate is fitted in such a way as to prevent any possibility of a flame striking the glass.

Cocks on fuel pipes. In order to isolate the fuel tank in event of fire, a cock must be fitted to the fuel tank where the fuel pipe leaves, and the cock must be easily operated at all times without moving heavy gear, or lifting any main floor boards. When the fuel tanks are remote from the driving position and fuel is gravity fed to the engine, another cock, in an accessible position in relation to the driving position, must be fitted if required.

Exhaust pipe, etc. The cylinders and exhaust pipe must be effectively cooled; in the case of air-cooled engines, and where water is not passed through the exhaust pipe, the exhaust pipe must be effectively lagged.

Silencer. The noise of the exhaust must be effectively suppressed, provided that any officer of the Conservators inspecting the launch may exercise his discretion as to the necessity of fitting a silencer. No form of exhaust cut-out may be used.

Engine tray. An oil-tight engine tray, made of metal or other approved material, the sides of which must be carried up as high as the propeller shaft will permit, must be fitted beneath the engine (if more than one, beneath each engine) so as to prevent leakage of lubricating oil escaping into any other part of the launch. Where necessary, a similar tray to be fitted under the gear box. In the case of a metal hull a tray is not required if oil-tight bulkheads are fitted fore and aft of the engine.

Electric leads, etc. Electric leads must be properly supported and insulated.

Auto-vac. Where an Auto-vac is fitted, and is very close to, or above the engine, it must be efficiently baffled off by steel and/or asbestos plates in such a manner as to prevent any flame from the engine making contact with the Auto-vac.

Batteries. All batteries must be securely installed and covered to prevent accidental movement and damage. No battery may be fitted beneath any petrol cock, tank, or filter unless an efficient baffle plate is interposed.

Part II: OUTBOARD MOTORS

Carburettors. Where the fuel used is petrol unmixed with oil a drip tray must be fitted entirely in accordance with the first paragraph of Part I of this Specification.

Fuel pipes. A cock must be fitted to the fuel feed pipe where it leaves the fuel tank, and must be efficiently brazed into the tank, or screwed into the tank with an approved washer, in such a manner in every case as to make an oil and spirit tight joint.

Silencer. The noise of exhaust must be effectively silenced. A cut-out may only be used for starting purposes.

Fuel tanks. Fuel tanks and cocks must be suitably protected against accidental damage from ramming. Separate fuel tanks, carried inboard and connected by approved flexible piping to the engine carburettor, may be used, provided that no unauthorised modifications are made to the equipment as supplied by the manufacturers.

Part III: FIRE EXTINGUISHING EQUIPMENT

Owners of launches must ensure that efficient and approved fire extinguishing equipment is carried and maintained on board at all times.

Part IV: BOTTLED GAS APPLIANCES AND INSTALLATIONS

(This section is omitted as it is outside the scope of the present book.)

Part V: COOKING AND HEATING APPLIANCES

Domestic cooking or heating appliances (whether using electricity or solid, liquid or gaseous fuel) must not be placed or used in close proximity to fuel containers or engines. Woodwork and other combustible materials adjacent to all such appliances must be suitably insulated or treated with incombustible materials against excess heat and all flues must be effectively insulated where necessary.

The Yachting Section of Lloyd's Register of Shipping has issued a useful series of leaflets giving brief hints on boat care and maintenance. The recommendations pertaining to engines and electrical installations are very much in line with those made earlier in this book, but some extracts from the leaflets are reproduced below (with the permission of Lloyd's Register of Shipping) as a matter of interest.

PROCEDURE BEFORE STARTING ENGINE

1. To reduce fire and explosion risks the machinery space should be thoroughly ventilated and the bilges clean and free from petrol, paraffin and fuel oil. The extraction fan should be used to clear the lower part of the machinery space of petrol vapour and Calor gas.

2. It is particularly important that the piping, fittings and joints of Calor gas installations are maintained in good condition. The master valve on the Calor gas container should be kept shut whenever gas is not being used.

3. The fire extinguishing appliances should be in efficient condition and readily available.

4. Fuel and lubricating oil should be more than adequate for the intended voyage. Check the level of the oil in the engine sump.

5. Drain off any water or sediment in the fuel and lubricating oil tanks.

6. Check that the engine holding-down bolts are tight.

7. Examine and renew where necessary the engine exhaust pipe lagging, particularly where the pipe passes through lockers.

8. Where the propeller shaft is lubricated with grease, the stern tube should be charged full of grease or filled with oil in the case of oil lubricated propeller shafts.

9. Shafting and propeller should be clear of obstructions and free to turn.

10. Turn engine, reverse-reduction gear, shafting and propeller by hand or by barring round to ensure that there is no obstruction.

11. Reverse-reduction gear should then be placed in neutral position.

12. Clear cooling water sea inlet strainers, fuel and lubricating oil filters and bilge suction strums to ensure free flow. When the engine cooling is by means of a closed system, e.g. radiator and fan, see that there is adequate water in the system.

13. Open cooling water sea inlet and discharge valves and cocks and see that clips on hoses joining closing length of pipes are securely fastened and that the hose connexions are in good order and water-tight.

14. Open valve for fuel supply to engine.

15. Prime fuel and lubricating oil systems.
16. Check that the bilge pumps are in good working order.

PROCEDURE FOR SEASONAL LAYING-UP OF ENGINE

In addition to carrying out the instructions contained in the engine maker's operation and maintenance manual, the owner should satisfy himself regarding the following:

1. Drain lubricating oil from engine sump and reverse-reduction gear case and refill with new oil. Run engine and gearing for short period to distribute oil.

2. Drain petrol from tank.

3. If it is inconvenient to remove petrol, measures should be taken to avoid leakages. All valves and cocks in the petrol system should be closed tightly and the machinery space well ventilated. The bilges should be cleaned and any petrol vapour there and in other confined spaces should be cleared by means of the extraction pump.

4. Drain completely the engine cooling water system including pipes and fittings and thus remove the danger of damage by frost.

5. Shut all sea inlet and discharge valves and cocks and if the yacht is left afloat screw down the glands of these valves and cocks, also the stern gland.

6. Exposed metal parts such as intermediate shafting should be coated with oil or grease.

7. Turn engine periodically and leave cranks in different angular positions on each occasion.

8. Check that hand operated bilge pump is in good working condition.

9. Check that fire extinguishing appliances are in efficient condition and readily available.

10. Remove batteries ashore for charging maintenance.

11. Remove Calor gas container ashore.

12. It is advisable to remove electrical apparatus such as magnetos, distributors, ignition coils and their cables for storage in a dry place.

ELECTRICAL INSTALLATIONS

Distribution. This should be carried out with the fully insulated system, i.e. two insulated conductors for each circuit and with the battery or dynamo circuits fully insulated. The disadvantage of earthing one pole of the battery or dynamo is that one fault is all that is necessary to put the respective circuit out of action. With the fully insulated two-wire system two faults are required to put the circuit out of action.

Cable. Conductors should be stranded, or in the smaller sizes they may be solid. Stranded conductors are mechanically stronger than solid conductors and they should always be used in spite of the slightly increased cost. In all cases where vibration may occur, such as between a generator and a switchboard or between a starter motor and a battery, stranded conductors are essential.

Rubber insulation has been used with success for many years and is still widely used, although polyvinylchloride (PVC) is now achieving some popularity as it is more resistant than rubber to the action of oil or acid.

The cable should be sheathed with lead alloy, tough rubber or, in the case of PVC insulation, a PVC sheath. In circuits which are likely to be permanently wet (i.e. nearly all circuits in a small yacht) a metal sheath, e.g. lead alloy, is strongly recommended. Conduit is a good mechanical protection for cable if the increase in cost and weight can be tolerated.

Fittings. Many of the attractive fittings on the market are not suitable for marine use, especially in small yachts where salt air rapidly corrodes thin steel fittings even if chromium plated. The only satisfactory fittings are those made of non-ferrous metal. Chromium plated brass fittings give good appearance and have high corrosion resistance. All electrical fittings exposed to the weather must be fitted with watertight glands for the cable entries, and watertightness should be ensured for successful operation.

Care should be taken with choice of switches. In the smaller switches the contacts are very prone to corrosion, whereas in the larger switches the contacts usually have a "wiping" action which helps to keep them clean. In exposed positions watertight switches only should be used, with packed watertight cable glands. All plugs and sockets, in positions such as those for connecting navigation lights, should be watertight and the sockets should be provided with blank caps to keep the socket dry when not in use. Where a watertight socket is fitted on deck it should be combined with a metal deck tube for the cables passing through the deck. Screwing the flange of a socket to a deck plank without using such a deck tube is not recommended.

Care and Maintenance. Frequently the electrical installation in a small yacht is the most neglected and this may lead to inconvenience or even serious trouble. All parts of the installation should be protected against moisture. Even internal fittings are subject to dampness which will cause corrosion and failure if not attended to. They should be kept as dry as possible, wiped dry at frequent intervals, and external fittings should be protected by smearing with Vaseline. Bilges should be kept dry, especially when the yacht is laid up or after a week-end trip when there is the greatest temptation not to bother.

Cleanliness is most important. Dirt and fluff should not be allowed to accumulate, especially on switchgear and machines, for it quickly absorbs oil mist and becomes felt-like. Vibration quickly causes screws and bolts to work loose, lock nuts or lock washers should be fitted.

Index

Page numbers in italics refer to illustrations